SAVAGE SEAS

SAVAGE SEAS

ROSEMARY KINGSLAND

GRANADA
MEDIA

B■XTREE

First published in Great Britain in 1999 by Boxtree

an imprint of Macmillan Publishers Ltd
25 Eccleston Place, London, SW1W 9NF
and Basingstoke

Associated companies throughout the world

ISBN 0 7522 1349 0

Inside page design by DW Design
Colour Origination by Speedscan, Basildon, Essex
Printed and bound in Italy by New Interlitho

Published in association with Granada Television and
Thirteen: WNET, New York

contents

preface

Wherever we are from, we cannot resist the call of the sea. Who, in their life, has not stood on a sandy shoreline, hypnotized by the sound, the smell, and the scale of the oceans? And when the surf is high – dark storm-sent waves assaulting piers and harbours, dunes and fragile craft – who has not felt dwarfed by a power they had never fully realized was there?

For most of us, most of the time, these periodic, primeval echoes of our ancient relationship with the sea are enough. Our lives on solid ground seem sufficiently fraught without the terrors of a 60-foot wave, or an Atlantic cloud of freezing fog. A holiday ferry or a winter stroll along the promenade are the closest we get to our savage seas.

Yet our climate and our history, our diet and our coastline, even perhaps our character have been defined by the sea, in ways we rarely appreciate and sometimes do not even understand.

In its ambitious documentary trilogy, Granada Television has already looked at the weather, and at earthquakes and volcanoes, in *Savage Skies* and *Savage Earth*. Filmed on every continent, in every season, and screened around the world, these programmes have explored the relationship between mankind and the immense natural forces which shape our life and our planet. This book and its companion ITV series, *Savage Seas*, are the third leg of a fascinating journey.

Survivors and sailors, surfers and submariners, scientists and lifeboatmen – through their stories we hope to build a better understanding of the deepest oceans.

The crab fisheries of the icy Bering Sea, the turquoise waters of the Bahamas, Hogsty Reef, the violent current of South Africa's 'Wild Coast', the epic surf of Cape Disappointment, the cyclone-generating Bay of Bengal – these, and many other places, are the ports of call for this book and these films.

Few of us wish to travel beyond that hypnotic ocean moment on some secret sandy shore... but hopefully anyone who has drawn a moment's pleasure from the mystery of the oceans will draw many more from reading this book.

Bill Jones
Executive Producer

Liz McLeod
Series Producer

introduction

If the sea holds a compelling fascination for us, it is because we are a part of it. The first glimmerings of life were born in the sea some 3,000 million years ago. Life was produced from non-life, from minerals and dissolved gases – and somehow, painfully slowly, yet in a seemingly miraculous way, living creatures emerged and evolved. The salts that surged through the waters of the deep oceans from pre-history to today still surge through our blood; each of us carries a salty stream of sodium, potassium and calcium in almost the same proportions as in sea water. We weep salty tears and we sweat salt. Even the gravitational pull of the moon, which affects the very tides of the sea, affects us: when the moon is full, we weigh less, and when it is dark, we are heavier.

Earliest man was terrified yet fascinated by the sea. Mythological stories grew about sea monsters; about the raging fires that encircled the oceans, flaming fiercely with all the horrors of hell where the waters ended. On a world that was considered flat, even up to the fifteenth century Europeans believed they would tip over the edge and into the terrifying unknown if they ventured too far away from land – indeed, if they ventured too far north or south of the Mediterranean, which was considered the centre of the world.

And yet the lure of the unknown was too fascinating. Man could not resist dipping his toe into the ocean; he could not resist building log boats to explore the coastlines. Little by little he journeyed further, and discovered that the sea fulfilled his wildest dreams, expectations – and fears. It was every bit as dangerous as imagined; every bit as wild and violent and as tempestuous as the legends had told. The more he explored, the more he found that the sea's mysteries and terrors only deepened. Often, his attempts to describe what he had seen were disbelieved.

Monsters and freak waves that can swallow entire ships at a single gulp and unimaginable depths – the stuff of legends – were accepted as scientific fact only in the twentieth century. The first freak wave was measured in 1933. Man first ventured almost seven miles to the bottom of the ocean in 1960. Giant clams and strange hot-water vents were first explored in 1977. The first giant squid was seen alive, swimming in the deep Atlantic, as recently as 1992. With every sighting, every 'proof', legends have become real.

But mysterious and fascinating as the sea is, it is also very dangerous and unpredictable. The power of the oceans dominates our planet, drives our climate and sustains us. It can also kill us. Every year the monsoon brings in great storm floods to cover vast tracts of land in Bangladesh, and has killed as many as half a million people in a single day; tsunami waves wipe out two or three hundred thousand coastal dwellers in the blink of an eye; an iceberg sinks the *Titanic*; collisions in freezing fog sink fishing fleets off Newfoundland's Grand Banks; in a five-day bloodbath, sharks attack and kill hundreds of shipwrecked servicemen; surging river bores capsize ships and swamp onlookers; submarines are crushed in the depths; oil tankers plunge into holes in the ocean down to the bottom of the sea, leaving no trace that they were ever there.

For every horror story there are also tales of great heroism, of a lifeboat crew that risked all in the roughest seas – and lost; of helicopters that send men out into the teeth of gales to save lives; of ordinary people going to the aid of those in peril. The story of the sea is a dramatic and ennobling one. Above all, it is one of great power and savagery.

chapter one
the water planet

A waterfall 10,000 feet high; connecting seas of two different heights; how the Romans nearly didn't conquer England; oysters that respond to the pull of the tide when they are in a tank 100 miles inland; a bride drowned by the sea at a party on the River Seine; plastic ducks and candy kisses washed up on beaches; vanishing ships – all these bizarre events have one thing in common: they reflect the mystery and the awesome power of the currents and tides of the sea.

CURRENTS: LOOPS AND GYRES

Opposite Man o' War Cove, Lulworth, in Dorset, England. In this panoramic view of the cove, the start of the continental shelf can just be seen as the beach falls steeply into the séa. The continental shelf is like an apron that skirts the land, formed from millions of years of debris, sand and gravel washed down by rivers or deposited by tides and currents. Waves often increase in size as they are compressed upwards when they hit the shelf after travelling across the ocean. The division between deep and shallow waters is often obvious by changes in colour of the sea.

The oceans, which cover the larger part of our planet, are not great slabs of water. They are an enormously complicated, self-regulating machine with all parts and all functions interlocking in a deeply complex way. Not only do the seas regulate our weather, but our very lives depend on their incredible science. By using currents, the oceans shift great blocks of warm water and cold water around the planet like a massive thermostat that constantly maintains a finely tuned balance. The oceans keep polar ice in its correct place. If all the ice melted water would cover the continents to a depth of several feet. So the oceans also regulate climate, rainfall, and their own depth.

Within the sea is as varied and dramatic a landscape as on the continents. Fathoms deep and out of sight are mountain ranges higher than Everest, submarine canyons and trenches deeper than the Grand Canyon, undulating hills, gentle valleys and vast plains. And in the last twenty years have been discovered hot springs and geysers like those in Yellowstone Park on a massive scale – deep sea vents which spew up hot water and tall mineral chimneys known as black smokers.

Continually, through the ages, frost, wind and rain break up the solid land of the continents and the islands. Massive glaciers during the ice ages have further ground down the land. Rivers and glaciers cut deep into the earth and carry all this debris down to the sea. And in the sea, strong currents carry abrasive sand, surging tides lift and throw stones and pebbles back and forth with a roar like a million dragons. Storms and surf leap up cliffs, grinding, carving, eroding, shaping the land, changing coastlines. It is an endless process that lays down sediments in an apron which skirts the land. This is the continental shelf. In some places, for example off Europe or around Newfoundland where the Grand Banks lie, it may extend for hundreds of miles; in other places, where deep, strong currents run parallel to the shore, scouring away sediments, it is a mini-skirt, hardly there at all. In most places, though, it slopes very gently downwards to a depth of about 600 feet or 100 fathoms below the surface.

Beyond this shelf is the continental slope; and beyond that – sometimes very abruptly – is a deep plunge of often several miles down to the abyssal plains, or the sea bed, although this is no smooth, flat bed but a very lumpy one indeed.

The mountains and valleys and plains of the abyss contribute to the way in which the sea works by directing and controlling deep ocean currents and internal tides, much as mountain ranges influence the winds that blow over them. Other controls are

In this aerial view of an atoll (the top of an ancient undersea volcano) currents as well as the depth of the sea can clearly be seen by a variation in colour.

Loops and Gyres

Loops and gyres relate to the circular or spiral motion of the currents, which in fact move and cross at different levels in a three-dimensional way, not just on the surface of the oceans as was once supposed. It is a very complicated pattern, with hot and cold currents keeping ocean water moving in constant motion around the world. These patterns are affected by the rotation of the Earth, the energy of the sun, wind and salt content and temperature of the oceans. They affect the climate – and, conversely, are affected by the climate.

Currents move horizontally (in any direction of the compass) and also at acute angles as cold, less dense (less saline) polar water plunges downwards and upwards in the Indian, Atlantic or Pacific oceans as it is heated up by the sun. If a single drop of water were to be followed on its entire journey around the oceans, it would take 1,000 years to return to its starting point – and on its long journey it would have varied from warm to cool, salty to less salty, and it would have moved through all the levels of the oceans, from the surface to the bottom.

the exchange of hot and cold water carried from equatorial to polar regions and back on the oceanic currents. As hot water rises to the surface to evaporate into rain clouds, cold water wells up from the deeps to take its place. There are layers of currents throughout the oceans, often going in opposite directions. The place where two currents meet, known as the convergence zone, makes a noticeable line, easily visible on the surface by a colour change.

Wherever two currents meet, especially if they differ in temperature or salinity, the effect can be dramatic, marked by thick fogs, zones of great turbulence, water constantly sinking and rising, violent eddies swirling and foam lines heaving at the surface. No wonder that in more superstitious times mariners believed that dragons were fighting below.

The primary driving force of the ocean currents is the winds. Modifying influences are the sun, the spinning of the Earth towards the east and the continental slopes of the great land masses which obstruct and deflect the currents. The spinning Earth exerts a deflecting force on everything that moves from a feather to a bullet, turning them to the right in the Northern Hemisphere and to the left in the Southern Hemisphere; thus ocean currents and major winds alike turn clockwise in the north and counter-clockwise in the south.

Exceptions are the Indian Ocean, where, ruled by the capricious monsoons, the currents shift towards land or away from land with the seasons; and the Antarctic Ocean – being a continuous band of water encircling the world with nothing in the way, its waters are constantly driven into the east and northeast by winds from the west and southwest (as round-the-world yachtsmen find to their occasional advantage if the weather is kind, which usually it isn't). Here, the currents are sped along by the vast quantities of fresh water pouring in from melting ice.

The most powerful currents, and those best known to seafarers through the ages, are the equatorial currents on either side of the Equator, running in the same direction, and the counter current which runs in the opposite direction along the Equator itself. Other important local, but powerful, currents are, in southern latitudes, the cold Benguela Current welling up from the Antarctic regions to cool down the shores and bring rich nutrients and great shoals of cold-water fish to West Africa; and the icy Humboldt Current which does the same for the western coast of South America. In the north are the polar Oyashio Current which flows around Japan, the Bering Sea and Alaska on the western side of the United States; and in the east, the equally icy Labrador Current which brings icebergs to Greenland, much of Canada and the St Lawrence Seaway.

Then there is the Gulf Stream. Known as the mightiest river in the world with a current more rapid than the Mississippi or Amazon rivers and a volume 1,000 times greater, rising from the bowels of the Earth in the tropics, it flows all the way to the Arctic, casting a benign warmth over the whole of western Europe.

Unexpectedly, we learn that it was Benjamin Franklin who discovered the Gulf Stream. 'I do not remember when I could not read,' he wrote, having read more books on every subject under the sun by the age of seventeen than many adults in their entire lives.

A founding father of the United States, a writer, a publisher, an inventor and a scientist, it was as deputy postmaster general of North America that Franklin's questioning mind was concerned with why American postal ships could make the journey to England from the colonies days, if not weeks, faster than the English merchant ships. The English authorities were amazed each time the post seemed to speed like a bird on the wing when entrusted to mere Americans and they wrote to Franklin, who consulted his cousin, Timothy Folger. Folger happened to be a whaling ship captain sailing out of Nuntucket and he knew about the Gulf Stream – as did the Spaniards when they ruled the New World waves.

Pleased with his findings, Franklin sent a chart to the English authorities, who promptly ignored it. However, during an Atlantic voyage in 1775 Franklin took temperature measurements of the water

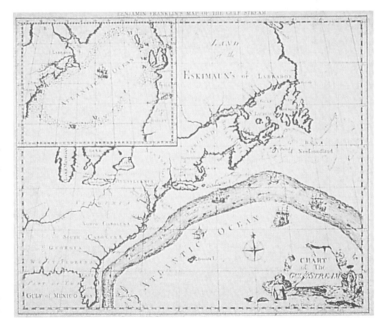

The first chart of the Gulf Stream, drawn by Benjamin Franklin, clearly showing this swift, warm current that flows from the Gulf of Mexico, past New York and across the Atlantic towards the UK. It influences the climate of Europe, making it milder than it would otherwise be.

Benjamin Franklin (1706–1790): US President, man of letters, and the first to map the Gulf Stream. (Portrait by Joseph Siffred Duplessis.)

several times a day. He was to repeat his experiments during subsequent voyages, right through the 1776 War of Independence and beyond, publishing *Maritime Observations* in Philadelphia. For the first time, information about the Gulf Stream was in print.

Voyage into the Sea of Darkness

Ancient mariners called all unknown waters the Sea of Darkness; but exploration is in human genes, and timidly men still dipped their paddles into the sea and full of trepidation headed out beyond the reassuring sight of land. We don't know who were the earliest explorers. Possibly there were a few accidents when fishermen were swept away in their fragile crafts to land on some far-flung island or continent. Driftwood coming in with strange objects and animals floating on it might have stimulated fear or curiosity or a mixture of both. But it seems that the first journeys were intentional – and far earlier than ever thought possible.

Early in 1998 an astonishing find on a remote island in the Pacific seems to prove that ape-men ventured forth on ancient currents into the unknown. It is 800,000 to 900,000 years ago that *Homo erectus,* a shorter, more ape-like predecessor of *Homo sapiens,* is thought to have poled a raft to the island of Flores in Eastern Indonesia from the southeast Asian mainland.

Dr Mike Morwood, a fossil expert of the Department of Archaeology and Palaeo-anthropology at the University of New England in New South Wales, and his team have unearthed fourteen stone tools on Flores, which could have only been reached by crossing the sea. Apart from anything else, this awesome find will revolutionize thinking on human evolution: it had always been assumed that it was only 100,000 years or so ago that our ancestors developed the intelligence needed to take to the seas. The evidence now is that they were clever enough to build and navigate seagoing rafts, probably from bamboo poles lashed together with vines, and to communicate with each other clearly enough both to construct rafts and to discuss where they would go.

Dr Morwood says: 'This is quite remarkable because we had thought that man made his way from the southeast Asian mainland to Australia much later, about 60,000 years ago, but it is now possible he made the journey by sea much earlier.'

Computer simulations have shown that such a raft could have reached the Australian mainland in seven to ten days, even without a sail, following the currents. However, the seas in that region are prone to fierce storms, and sharks abound. Perhaps more mariners were lost at sea than ever arrived.

There is a massive gap from *Homo erectus* to modern man; and indeed hundreds of thousands of years of navigational history are cloaked in mystery. The first modern navigators that we know about could have been pirates. Robbers have sailed and sacked the seas for at least 7,000 years, starting in the Persian Gulf. Some went to sea on rafts supported by inflated pigskin bladders, shooting poison arrows at their victims. A Persian king was known as Lord of the Shoulders because he pierced captured pirates through the shoulders and strung them together to prevent escape.

Wall paintings from ancient Egypt show galley slaves rowing ships on voyages to far-off lands, bringing back goods by trade or piracy. It is known that Egyptians sailed down the east coast of Africa and perhaps went to India. The Minoans, whose King, Daedalus, was said to have built a flying machine, ranged as far west as Spain, taking with them King Minos's cult of the bull. Their lavish

kingdom was destroyed suddenly by an earthquake in 1400 BC, leaving the way open for the Phoenicians to rise as the next great maritime power.

Phoenicians, the Canaanites of the Old Testament, built Tyre after the Israelites conquered their strongholds of Jerusalem and Jericho. With no land and enemies to their back, the Phoenicians became pirates, masters of the Mediterranean for a thousand years and traded for tin as far as Britain. They even captured Odysseus in an attempt to sell him as a slave. The Greek historian Herodotus tells how around 600 BC Pharaoh Necho commissioned the Phoenicians to circumnavigate Africa. On their return, three years later, they described the path of the sun – different in the Southern Hemisphere – but Herodotus dismissed their claim. Eventually, of course, what they had said about the sun was found to be true – and they could not have known unless

Above The Phoenicians were masters of the known seas for a thousand years. They were the first to use currents to take them from the Middle East as far as Britain, where they traded for Cornish tin.

Below A wall painting of Ancient Egyptian seafarers. In boats like these they ranged down the east coast of Africa, or even further afield, to trade.

they had gone. It is said that perhaps they discovered Brazil in 531 BC, rowing their three-tiered ships along the Equatorial Current.

But most of these voyages, while teaching seamanship, did not open up the vast reaches of the oceans to mariners. Even Alexander the Great, who had boldly gone across most of Asia, marched back the same way. It was his men who built boats in India to sail home – clinging close to shore. The open sea remained a mystery until the Vikings set sail, first for Iceland and to Vinland which was somewhere in North America.

A century before the Portuguese Vasco da Gama sailed around Africa, or the Spanish and the English had crossed the Atlantic to the New World, China's Ming dynasty ruled the seas, travelling vast distances with treasure-junks that were an incredible 442 feet long and 180 feet wide. They carried crews of 500 men at a time when the tiny European ships carried 20 or perhaps 30 men. With a fleet of over 250 war-junks, 62 treasure-junks to carry back loot he had captured and 29,000 soldiers, Admiral Cheng Ho was sent on many trading and punitive expeditions throughout the Eastern seas from Japan to India, Persia and Africa. In fact Cheng Ho said that he had sailed as far as Britain but, curiously, never landed. However, it is thought that the Chinese, who recorded a voyage made in AD 459 by Hui Shen and four other Buddhist monks, accidentally stumbled across

America in their search for an earthly paradise by using the Kuroshio Current, which flows eastwards from Japan across the Pacific.

The Wayfinders

But the greatest mariners of all were the Polynesians, a mysterious race who seemed to arrive from nowhere. Around 2,500 to 3,000 years ago, they used their knowledge of navigation, ocean currents and swells, prevailing winds, the stars, sun and moon and flights of birds to range over more than 20 million square miles of ocean with only two units of land for every 100 of water, colonizing almost every inhabitable island in the vast Pacific, from Easter Island to New Zealand and, finally, Hawaii between AD 250 and 500. They called their system the 'Wayfinding' technique. Having noticed that waves react differently when approaching an island, they knew from 100 miles away whether an island lay ahead simply by kneeling in their boats and feeling the water for the slightest sense of rebound. Their tool for teaching wave science was a natural compass they called a *mattang*, which was a simple interlocking web of bamboo sticks that gave them the rising and setting points of the stars. A navigator would train for several years to master these techniques, gaining an instinctive feel for the ocean while memorizing lists of star paths from one island to another.

Norwegian mariner and anthropologist Thor Heyerdahl thought the Polynesians had originally come from South America, and constructed the *Kon Tiki*, a balsa raft, on

Main picture King Manuel I of Portugal blesses Vasco da Gama (kneeling with flag) and his expedition before they set out on their perilous journey around Africa and across the Indian Ocean. It was to be two years before they returned safely, having opened the route east.

Lake Titicaca to prove his theory that they could have sailed vast distances west to colonize Polynesia. More vocal sceptics did not believe that the navigation achievements of the Polynesians were possible at all, arguing that islands like Hawaii were discovered by accident.

In 1976, Hawaiians built a 62-foot replica sailing canoe, the *Hokule'a,* and sailed it from Maui to Tahiti without compass or sextant. In 1985–7 they went on a 16,000-mile Pacific island-hopping trip, the Voyage of Rediscovery, to ram home their point.

From Arsenic to Candy Kisses: Flotsam and Jetsam

In 310 BC the Greek philosopher Theophrastus threw bottles into the sea to prove his theory that the Mediterranean had been formed by the inflow of water from the Atlantic. Many centuries later, British intelligence agents used bottles to send back messages to the Admiralty. An 'Official Uncorker of Ocean Bottles' held office at the court of Elizabeth I – and it was a capital offence for anyone else to open bottles washed up on beaches. This century a dishwasher picked up a drift bottle containing a note written thirteen years earlier by Singer sewing machine heiress, Daisy Alexander. The note simply said, 'I leave my entire estate to the lucky person who finds this bottle and my attorney, Barry Cohen, share and share alike.' The fortune: $12 million.

The record for a bottle bobbing its way around the world was the one thrown into the sea by Matsuyuma, a Japanese treasure hunter who was shipwrecked on a Pacific reef with forty-four companions. Before they all perished, he sent his last message out, carved on a piece of wood and sealed in a bottle. Almost 150 years later, it washed up in the village where he was born. Each year, the US Coast and Geodetic Survey drop in the sea thousands of bottles called drogues or drifters containing questionnaires that help survey the currents. Finders are asked to fill in the details of where and when found.

With a fascinating mix of theory and reality, mariners have known for centuries where the ocean currents are. But for scientists the challenge had been to understand precisely how they work. An unlikely step forward came at the end of 1990 with an unexpected find by an Oregon beachcomber – golf shoes.

In May 1990, during a severe storm in the Pacific, twenty-one deck cargo containers, each approximately 40 feet long, were lost overboard from a Korean container ship, the *Hansa Carrier.* The cargo was 39,466 pairs of Nike athletic shoes, including the scores of golf shoes washed up on the beaches of Washington, Oregon and British Columbia some six months to a year later. The shoes, with a retail value of $100 a pair, were covered in oil and barnacles, but after a good scrub were wearable. Beach residents started up flourishing swap meets to match up pairs.

Oregon artist and shoe collector Steve McLeod matched up several pairs: 'It all started on the beach... you find shoes on the beach all the time, like toothbrushes. I didn't think anything of them, even though they'd been out there for a long time. But over a period of three or four days I saw half a dozen golf shoes and I said, how can these be here? Was it like a tidal wave on a golf course or something? Then I put two and two together and said, they must have come off a container ship.'

Oceanographer Dr Curtis Ebbesmeyer of Seattle read a newspaper article on the beach Nikes. He was intrigued and realized that 78,932 shoes was a very large number of drifting objects, comparable to the 33,869 drift bottles used in a 1956–9 study of North Pacific currents. He contacted McLeod, who has information on locations and data for some 1,600 shoes that had been found between northern California and Queen Charlotte Islands in British Columbia.

Other beachcombers were invited to join in the saga and Ebbesmeyer started work, mapping and logging where batches of more than 100 or more shoes had turned up. A computer model – the Ocean Surface Current Simulations (OSCURS), run by Dr James Ingraham of the National Marine Fisheries Service – was used to predict the drift, and found to match up perfectly with predicted currents.

Ebbesmeyer knew details of the Nike ship and the cargo but he wanted some stronger proof, some link. 'I started poking around and if you look inside a sneaker, there's a number and if you give me that number I can trace it to the container that fell overboard. I learned from beachcombers where they were washing up and a colleague of mine had a model that could predict this. I faxed him the info of where and when the spill occurred and asked him to run his computer model and it was dead on. It was a blind test.'

What the model did was establish the exact course and speed of the Pacific Current from the point where the cargo had gone overboard to whichever part of the coast the shoes washed up. A thousand containers are lost at sea every year, so many that they have become a major shipping hazard; but now they also offered the possibility of a breakthrough in ocean science – and an unlikely alliance between scientists and beachcombers.

The confirmation came with the loss of another vessel in 1994 when the *Hyundai Seattle* caught fire in the Pacific. About fifty containers fell overboard, including 38,000 pieces of hockey equipment in two of the containers. Ebbesmeyer's colleague ran his computer model and it showed that items from the spill should wash up in Vancouver Island on 30 January.

'That's today!' Ebbesmeyer said.

Steve McLeod happened to be on the beach that day and had found a couple of shin-guards and some gloves. He telephoned Ebbesmeyer: 'I think I've got something for you. He said, "You found some hockey gloves?" You could have knocked me over with a feather.'

What the computer model bears out is a complete, clockwise circulation of the North Pacific's waters every seven years. But the movement is not a regular one. It has mysterious fits and starts. Ebbesmeyer says the cycle in the Pacific operates like the hands of a clock that are occasionally not too steady. In the North Pacific it's as if one time it takes three hours to go around and the next time it takes 30 minutes. 'It's a very unsteady clock and we think it has a lot to do with the world's climate.'

The oceans and the atmosphere are intimately related and both are affected by the Earth's motion. As the Earth spins on its axis it causes both air and water to twist into

There is a degree of curiosity and excitement about beachcombing, as Steve McLeod *(left)* and Dr Curtis Ebbesmeyer *(right)* can confirm as they search for debris on a stormy Oregon beach. There is also interesting science: the origin of flotsam and jetsam washed up can give us information about ocean currents.

spiral patterns or vortexes. The ocean currents follow these patterns, joining together in ways that are still only half understood.

Ebbesmeyer says:

'When you see waves all around you, the ocean looks like there's no pattern to it. But if you look at all the information you find that the oceans are pretty organized... even though there's some chaos. You have the Pacific going around clockwise. The Arctic Ocean has a couple of big vortexes; the Atlantic Ocean has two of them. The surface waters have this wonderful vortex structure... it's really beautiful to behold. When you look at Jupiter you see that big red spot. Earth has its own red spot but you can't see it. It's the North Pacific vortex. It is, perhaps, Earth's biggest feature – only you can't see it because it's a current.'

We don't have a clear picture of how the ocean's spiral currents connect. As much information as possible and more container flotsam are helping to complete that very complex picture. Suitably, in 1992 a shipment of plastic bath-toys, some 30,000 yellow ducks, blue turtles, red beavers and green frogs, jumped ship in mid-Pacific. Carried fast by a current, they reached Alaska in just eight months. As of 1998 they were crossing the Arctic Ocean and looked set to swim all the way into the Atlantic.

There is a degree of excitement within the beachcombing community to see a hobby materialize into real science. Ebbesmeyer says: 'We had never run an object in the computer model that drifted this fast in front of the wind. These are really fast, really tough little critters. Now the computer model shows them over the North Pole.'

They are due to come out of the Arctic Ocean and get into the North Atlantic in about 2005 or so. Britain is going to have an armada of possibly the best travelled yellow plastic ducks in the world – and the strange sightings are speeding up, with the loss in February 1997 of millions of Lego pieces to a freak wave as the *Tokio Express* steamed into mountainous water 20 miles off Land's End, England. The wave, described by the captain as a 'once-in-a-100-years phenomenon', tilted the ship 60 degrees one way then 40 degrees back – a total arc of 100 degrees, springing sixty-two containers overboard. Each one held 4,756,940 Lego plastic pieces en route from Rotterdam to New York. Ironically, the kits depicted sea adventures.

Children in England found octopuses, dragons, sea grass and diver flippers – but possibly only a few pieces escaped a watery grave since all the kits were carefully packed. If they do float out of their packaging, the Lego toys should get locked into the North Atlantic gyre and arrive along Florida, Georgia and the Carolinas. Some might possibly float northward past Norway into the Arctic Ocean, following the fabled Northeast Passage through the coastal waters of northern Siberia, arriving in Alaska after a dozen years or so. From Alaska, currents might carry a few toys southward to Japan and then across the North Pacific Ocean to British Columbia, Washington, Oregon and California to join any golf shoes and sneakers still adrift. By the year 2020 currents will have distributed Lego elements throughout much of the Northern Hemisphere.

Although tiny, there is a good chance that the Lego pieces will be together in large groups, perhaps noticeable first by the bright yellow miniature rafts. As Ebbesmeyer says: 'Flotsam, like birds of a feather, flocks together . . .'

As if plastic ducks and Lego pirates aren't curious enough, chocolate and candy was lost from the 816-foot container ship, *Pol American,* in New England's 1997 April Fool blizzard 11 miles off Cape Cod. Within days, candied beaches were reported on Nantucket Island.

However, not all flotsam and jetsam are so sweet. In 1991, after storm seas struck the *Santa Clara I,* a container ship bound for Baltimore, coast guards were put on full alert when twenty-one containers fell into New York Bight, four of which held arsenic trioxide, used in insecticide, herbicides and wood preservatives. An official report stated: 'A single dose of arsenic trioxide no larger than the size of an aspirin tablet is lethal to humans.'

Inside the containers were 414 drums with enough arsenic to produce 170 million tablets, capable of killing half the US population – to say nothing of the ocean's. At a cost of $4 million all the poison was salvaged. So, happily, instead of arsenic, Nantucket beachcombers recovered Hershey's chocolate Kisses.

Currents do not just move massive blocks of warm and cold water around the world; they are not just a conveyor belt for flotsam and jetsam – they can be dangerous in their own right when confronted with other currents or winds and tides in opposition: it is a case of a freight train meeting a steamroller on the track. Such a situation exists at Cape Horn, a notorious graveyard for ships since the days when great seamen like Drake and Magellan sailed around the world, and the Wild Coast of South Africa, east of the Cape of Good Hope.

The Wild Coast

Ships big and small, from yachts, ocean liners, tankers and container ships, regularly run into difficulties off South Africa, where one of the most dangerous and notorious currents which sweeps down the east coast in a southerly direction collides with powerful winds and strong waves and tides going in the opposite direction around the Cape of Good Hope. This is a region where the continental shelf falls off very steeply into deep ocean, often giving rise to rogue waves of terrifying heights (see page 45). Yet despite all the known dangers, shipping continues to put itself at risk.

Around the southwest tip of southern Africa, west of the Cape of Good Hope, is the Skeleton Coast, so-called because of the wrecks of ships and the bleached bones of whales cast up on the lonely coastal desert by the ice-cold and fast-flowing Benguela Current, with its deadly cross-currents, heavy swells and thick fogs. Gale-force winds build mountainous waves. It is the reverse image of the Wild Coast, on the opposite side of the continent – site of one of the greatest maritime mysteries of the twentieth century: the disappearance of an entire ship together with her passengers and crew.

When the SS *Waratah* left Durban in July 1909 with more than 200 people on board, she was on only her second voyage, heading home from Australia to Britain. Weighing just over 9,000 tons, she was laden with a cargo of some 10,000 tons of flour and frozen meat, in effect doubling her weight – but it was not an unsafe weight.

Built on the Clyde, this brand-new steamship was the pride of the Blue Anchor shipping line. Her captain, Josiah Ilberry, had over forty years' experience at sea. Yet within twenty-four hours he, his passengers and crew and his ship had vanished. No trace of them has ever been found. Some might say that the name *Waratah* is an unlucky one. Named after the pretty red blossom of an Australian tree, several ships bearing that name were lost: one in 1848, two in 1887 and another in 1894.

Emlyn Brown is an underwater salvage expert who has been researching the *Waratah* for nearly twenty years and believes he is about to find her last resting place beneath the waves. He says: 'The big question with the *Waratah* is, "How is it possible

An artist's impression of the *Nemesis*, a war steamer of the East India line, surviving wild storms along the Agulhas current. Tossed in huge waves which threaten to overwhelm it, the East India Company's iron war steamer struggles to stay afloat. In 1841 *Nemesis* was the first iron ship to sail around the Cape of Good Hope.

that a ship, sailing the relatively short distance from Durban to Cape Town, can simply disappear?" I've always been drawn to the sea and the *Waratah* is a story that to me, when I first read it, was irresistible. I have never for one moment doubted that the *Waratah* has been reserved for me to find and explore.'

But to begin to work out how this large ship met her end, we need to look not to the sea bed where she now lies, but to the place where the sea meets the shore.

This region has been called the Wild Coast with good reason. From the massive mountains marching along the east coast of Africa, a narrow continental shelf plunges 600 feet down to the ocean bed. As the Indian Ocean surges shorewards it breaks against the underwater shelf, producing waves of exceptional height and power (see the way in which waves work, page 57). But this coast has a second distinctive feature: it is swept by one of the fiercest ocean currents in the world.

The Agulhas Current is like a mighty river within the sea itself. A torrent of water 60 miles wide and one mile deep rushes down the coast at up to 10 feet a second. Skippers have always ridden this current to save time and fuel – even though experience has taught most of them that this can be a very dangerous ride indeed. Many of them hope to balance speed with caution, getting off that train before it meets the steamroller – the wind and the waves that rush towards the tip of South Africa from every direction.

Wave measurements made from a research ship north of Durban in the early 1970s

Top Strong currents and opposing winds combine to hurl high waves at rocks off Cape Agulhas on South Africa's Wild Coast – the graveyard of many ships.

Above Seen here in calm seas, the SS *Waratah* vanished suddenly and mysteriously off South Africa's Wild Coast in 1909. Was she sunk by one of the 100-foot freak waves occasionally created where the powerful Agulhas Current confronts opposing storm-driven waves?

showed that wave energy almost doubled here as the ship moved into the current. This enhancement of the wave heights was obeying a recognized wave/current interaction which related to a number of wave-related disasters in this area of the sea. The fact that the current is warm relative to adjacent waters makes it easy to identify the current and its boundaries on infrared images of surface temperature. It has been seen that the current is not straight and does not follow the 600-foot shelf break exactly. There is a cyclonic (clockwise in the Southern Hemisphere) offshore meander which slowly moves downstream of the current as a solitary wave-like pulse named the 'Natal Pulse' after its place of origin. Other small scallops of cross-current activity cut across the main current at varying speeds. In the region south of Africa, large, warm anticyclonic eddies can 'bud off' to form the basis of storms. Southwesterly winds, against the flow of the current, generate large waves. The whole region is in a permanent state of flux and confusion: a recipe for disaster after disaster.

For Captain Ilberry of the *Waratah*, as for the skippers of today, good seamanship dictated that he should use this ferocious current, along the 100-fathom line that separates the coastal shelf from the deep ocean (see the notes on the 100-fathom line on page 53).

Allan Parkinson, a master mariner of many years' experience and Head of Maritime Studies at Natal Technikon in Durban, teaches meteorology, maritime law, seamanship and navigation to students who want to pursue a career at sea. He spent sixteen years in the Merchant Marine himself, rising to become a ship's master, and has personal experience of South Africa's dangerous seas. For that reason, he is able to demystify the facts:

> 'The Agulhas Current is basically a large body of water, moving rapidly down the east coast of South Africa at between 2 and 5 knots speed. High pressure systems to the northeast speed the seas up. When southwesterly winds meet this fast-moving current it creates friction between the air and seas, creating bigger waves. Occasionally this process can create the abnormal or so-called freak waves. Only in recent history, when ships have become both large and strong enough to survive such waves, has our knowledge begun to grow about this phenomenon.'

Parkinson states that the southwesterly winds are the precursor to potential danger. 'Any seaman with any sense will take heed of the warnings. If there's been a southwest blow for more than a day or two, keep off the 100-fathom line.'

For many ships' masters, the difference between getting home safely to port and ending up on the rocks seems obvious. The phrase *keeping a weather eye out* in this region can be more than just a phrase – it should be vital.

Parkinson says: 'I think people tend to underestimate the weather on the coast. The sea can be very calm and very pleasant and kind to you; but it can also develop a great rage and sometimes the time between the pleasantness and the rage of the sea can be a matter of hours.'

As the *Waratah* rode the current southwards she had the prevailing wind behind her – but the barometer was dropping fast. As the pressure fell, Captain Ilberry found himself heading into the teeth of a southwest wind straight from the Antarctic. Just before, he had overtaken the *Clan MacIntyre,* also heading towards London but at a slower pace. Onshore there was a single witness, a soldier, but his evidence was ignored, possibly because his unit, the Cape Mounted Riflemen, didn't want to get entangled with the sensationalism surrounding the ship's disappearance.

Trooper Joe Conquer was carrying out live shell practice near the mouth of the Xora River when he saw a ship 'proceeding very slowly in a southwesterly direction and making very heavy weather'. He watched the ship through a telescope and later he reported, 'I can still see her in my mind's eye. She was a ship of considerable tonnage with a single funnel, two masts, a black hull, the upper works painted yellow. I watched this ship crawling along and saw her roll to starboard and then, before she could right herself, a following wave rolled over her and I saw her no more.'

More recently, a cruise ship, the *Oceanos,* ran into very similar seas in almost the same spot. August is the middle of winter in the Southern Hemisphere, and, even though it is usually mild in South Africa, the weather comes from the icy reaches of the Antarctic far from the south.

Early in August 1991 in Cape Town harbour, the weather was taking a turn for the worse. Inside the breakwater, aboard the *Oceanos,* 580 people – passengers, crew and entertainers – were on a pleasure cruise up the Wild Coast to Durban. The captain wanted to keep to his schedule and despite the weather was reluctant to delay; but the sea swell was already daunting, even for hardened passengers like George and Gerda Walton, who were having a second honeymoon to celebrate George's retirement.

George says: 'Looking at the weather and looking at the sea as we went out, I was surprised that we were allowed to go out of the harbour because the seas were really rough. Even the pilot boat struggled to keep up with us.'

In fact, the seas were so rough that the harbour pilot aboard the *Oceanos* was almost unable to rejoin his boat, as Robin Boltman, one of the ship's entertainers (who has since been through another catastrophe when the cruise ship the *Achille Lauro* was set on fire in 1994), observed. 'The pilot boat eventually came alongside, or tried to get alongside. I was standing on the port wing of the bridge watching the pilot trying to get off. He battled – and after that, they decided to close the harbour.'

But that order came too late for the thirty-year-old *Oceanos.* She had been built for pleasure cruises in the Mediterranean; now for four days she was to battle steadily with the Agulhas Current – and pay the ultimate price. Ship's entertainers Moss and Tracy Hills were also apprehensive. In their experience aboard many ships, they had battled with storms. Tracy had previously broken an arm and gashed a leg open in one, so she knew the score. This storm seemed worse than usual. 'You could feel it was rough and the wind was very, very strong. We usually had a "sail-away" party on the deck. But we scrapped the whole idea and had the party in the lounge, where we tried to keep the passengers occupied. But the ship was bouncing about so much, it was very hard to keep them happy.'

Shortly after this photograph was taken, the luxury liner *Oceanos* slipped beneath the waves in fierce seas off South Africa's Wild Coast. Fortunately, all her passengers were rescued safely.

Robin Boltman described it: 'We were careering off the stage and then climbing back on again. We were trying to do a sing-along thing but were thrown off the stage. We were rocking and rolling. Thrown about left, right and centre.'

The seas were so high because the southerly current was fighting storm-driven waves crashing northwards. The *Oceanos* was not the only vessel battling through these chaotic waters, but she was the oldest. Unknown to them, the seas had already claimed a much newer vessel. The oil tanker *Mimosa* now lay drifting a few miles away, her steering smashed. She had radioed for help and, back in Cape Town, salvage master Ian Merriman was setting out on a bid to rescue her.

The conditions he found were extraordinary: 'We left in our normal 20 minutes' notice requirement. Sitting in the docks the weather was wonderful, mill-pond conditions, brilliant day. We got to beyond the breakwater and hit this terrific swell. As we got further down to Cape Agulhas we increased speed. Unfortunately, the swell size also increased. If you're at the bottom of one of those swells and you look up at the top I would say it was in excess of 30 metres [100 feet] – which is a hell of a swell. It's like being in a washing machine.'

But there was a need for urgency. There were nearly 400,000 tons of crude oil aboard the *Mimosa*. Each successive wave made it look more likely that it would end up in the sea in a pristine conservation area. A spill of that magnitude would have been an environmental catastrophe. Onshore currents would swamp Cape Town and Durban with crude oil. These same swells were also testing every 40-year-old nut and bolt in the *Oceanos*. As darkness fell, the swells found a weakness in her hull. In the lounge, the entertainers were still rocking and rolling, trying to entertain the passengers. All of a sudden the lights went out. They were at the mercy of the sea.

The entertainment staff were used to fielding problems – but they found the crew tight-lipped. Moss Hills took a camera to find out the trouble for himself: 'I couldn't get a straight answer from any of the officers, so I went down below. As I went down the stairs, I could hear the water... I could see it.' He videotaped himself, recording the disaster about to unfold: 'There's water everywhere, it's sloshing about from side to side. So I guess we're going down.'

One of the crew came round the corner and started shouting at Moss, asking him what he was doing there. Moss was saying, look at all this water and, bizarrely, the crewman was denying it existed even as he was wading through it.

Despite the inrush of water that was rapidly flooding the ship, no announcement was made to the passengers. It was left to the entertainers to keep them calm. Above, they could hear the davits launching the lifeboats, the grating sound of the metal arms, the lowering into the sea.

The mood was very edgy. Robin Boltman sums it up: 'You start to think, the Wild Coast... notorious seas... outside the wind's howling... and you think, sharks.'

The evacuation was disorganized; and still no alarm was given. It quickly became clear that it wasn't just passengers who were leaving the vessel. Robin says: 'We didn't have any emergency signals, or any abandon ship, or report to your muster station. Guys were coming back, saying the lifeboats are full of crew, the Greek crew were taking the prime spots. Then it really dawned that we are not going to get power back. This is it – we are going to sink.'

Both officers and crew seemed to have panicked. It was the ship's entertainers who had to take control. A few people were crying in the corner or saying a prayer, but generally, the passengers were very calm. Bit by bit, the entertainers just started taking over in lieu of any leadership from the captain, who was on board but who seemed divorced from reality. Moss Hills says: 'He acted like another passenger, sitting on the pool deck under the stairs, smoking away, unable to grasp the situation...'

Daybreak made the reality all too clear. The ship was keeling over under the weight of water. The movement was gradual but unstoppable. Glasses broke, chairs and people fell over as the ship gradually, almost imperceptibly, listed more and more. With daylight, when they saw the horizon it hit home that they were no longer horizontal. It was frightening. Many of them imagined that they would be pulled down by the suction of the sea as the ship sank.

In heavy seas, most of the lifeboats had left only half full; 228 people were still on board. Scared, none of them were aware that vessels were ploughing through the heavy seas towards them, including Ian Merriman on his salvage tug, about to be faced with a dilemma. The *Mimosa* was important because she was in a very critical condition – but now he was faced with a large number of passengers. Safety of life at sea comes first: Merriman felt he had two jobs in one to cope with.

As he approached the *Mimosa*, he could smell the fumes from a mile away. It was clear that the current and waves had dealt her a massive blow. The sea had opened a gaping hole in her hull and threatened to break the vessel apart. 'She was lying beam-on to the sea, wallowing around, decks continually awash, spewing oil... I think... she's broken her back. 360,000 tons of oil on our coast is not nice to think about. It would have been ecological genocide.'

Merriman had to stay with the *Mimosa* to attempt a salvage. The ferocity of the current was threatening two vessels, to bring both environmental disaster and massive loss of life. On the *Oceanos* the passengers now looked towards the skies for help. But their would-be rescuers would find the challenge a daunting one.

An Air Force helicopter had been scrambled from Durban, with two rescue divers on board. Navy diver Paul Whiley was preparing to assess the situation. 'The journey out was exciting until I saw how many people were on deck. It was quite frightening... I saw two, maybe three hundred people and looking at the way the vessel was listing, I realized we weren't going to get everybody off.'

The wind was blowing 60 knots. As the tilting deck heaved, the first problem the Navy divers faced was how to get themselves aboard. Moss Hills realized the problem. He went on to the deck, found some rope, tied it around his waist and around the one railing at such an extreme, vertical angle it was almost like abseiling, and as the divers swung past he managed to grab them and helped them down. They showed Moss a few hand signals and how to operate the helicopter lift. From that point, Moss and Tracy ran the helicopter rescue in the bows.

Two by two, people began to be lifted off, to be ferried to the distant coast. It seemed an impossible task. Moss says: 'With a few helicopters and quite a distance to travel to the shore, I really didn't think we'd get all the passengers off in time. It was an awful feeling because once we have taken over, you're committed, you can't abandon those passengers. We kept thinking, well, we have to get all these people off before we can get off. We're probably going to end up in the water.'

In fact, it was another passenger, George Walton, who fell in the sea. As the line of people snaked forward, Paul Whiley called down, telling George and Gerda that they were next in line. George held his wife's hands: 'Don't worry, within a minute it's going to be over.'

Paul had Gerda in one side of the harness and tried to get George on the other side, but the strap wouldn't go over his head. As they went up, the strap slipped and Gerda tried to hang on to him. It was obvious he was going to fall. George started to get heavier, then he slipped down. Finally, at 90 metres up, he was hanging on to Gerda's legs. The next thing, he was gone. He fell into the surging waves from the height of a twenty-storey building. Gerda's thoughts were that all the plans she and George had made for his retirement were gone. Now she was alone. But miraculously, he survived with just a broken toe, pulled out of the sea by a lifeboat from one of the rescue ships that shortly arrived.

Astonishingly, the *Oceanos* remained afloat long enough for everyone on board to be lifted off. George's fall was the only serious mishap. As the last ones were rescued, their elation was mixed with a sense of loss. Moss says: 'As we left, we flew around the side of the ship. We could see the whole bow area going under water. It's a terribly tragic sight because it's almost like a living thing.'

The *Oceanos* was past saving but her passengers were safe. And, despite the *Mimosa*'s colossal damage, Ian Merriman succeeded in taking her into tow. She and her cargo of crude oil survived the onslaught of waves and current; but Merriman knows how fine is the margin between success and disaster at sea. 'Only a fool wouldn't be frightened by the sea. I respect the sea. As long as you respect it you're all right. If you try to beat it, it will kill you.'

Eighty years on from the disappearance of the *Waratah*, the Agulhas Current had yielded up a sequence of ironies. Captain Ilberry, with forty years' service, certainly respected the sea – and yet his vessel was lost. The *Mimosa* survived, despite massive damage; yet the *Oceanos* slid to the bottom in the very waters where the *Waratah* had last been sighted. The passengers and crew aboard the *Oceanos* were spared; yet 200 souls aboard her ghostly predecessor were not. And despite the similar circumstances, the sinking of the *Oceanos* does not fully answer the question: what happened to the *Waratah*? In her final departure for the ocean depths, the *Oceanos* left behind a trail of debris to mark her passing: deck-chairs, ropes and personal belongings of every kind. The *Waratah* left not a single scrap.

Whatever swallowed her up whole as she ploughed through that Wild Coast storm must have been sudden, cataclysmic and total in its destructive energy.

Emlyn Brown believes he knows what it was – and that he has found the last resting place of the *Waratah*: 400 feet down on the sea bed, close to where Trooper Joe Conquer said he had seen her, he has found a wreck. But so strong is the Agulhas Current that repeated attempts have failed to get near it – and have brought divers close to disaster. If she is the *Waratah*, then the current in which she came to grief may yet prove to be her final guardian.

But why did the *Waratah*'s sinking leave no trace? Emlyn Brown thinks it was a rare event called a freak wave, before which is that dreadful phenomenon called a hole in the ocean. As a great wave piles unnaturally high with the accumulated energy of several waves, the sum of all their troughs is suddenly formed at its base. *It can be as much as 90 feet deep.* As the ground opens up during an earthquake, so the sea seems to gape its jaws – and the ship ploughs straight in. The enormous wave collapses on the deck of the ship, thousands of tons of dead-weight water sending it straight down

Emlyn Brown, salvage expert, ponders the fate of the *Waratah* close to the spot off the Transkei region of the Wild Coast where he believes the ship sank without trace, all lives lost.

to the bottom. It is so instantaneous, so complete, that nothing is left to tell the tale. (See page 45–66.)

After spending so long searching for the *Waratah*, Emlyn Brown feels an affinity with her drowned captain: 'Captain Ilberry would have seen a wall of green water. He would have looked out of the bridge and probably said, "Oh my God". And when that wave, that final wave, came over the bow of the ship, I don't think anyone inside the ship knew what hit them. The *Waratah* is a *Poseidon Adventure* for 211 passengers and crew.'

But out there, where a powerful current collides with wind, waves and weather – it could be that the sea is still waiting to swallow up another *Waratah* whole.

TIDES

Oysters are in such close harmony with the rise and fall of the tides – opening to feed when a high tide comes in to cover them, closing to protect themselves when the tide is out – that even when removed from the sea and put in a tank many miles away, they will behave as if they are still in the sea at home. In an experiment, oysters were taken from Long Island Sound 100 miles inland to a sealed and darkened tank. Scientists were fascinated to note that at first they followed their normal rhythm, opening and closing to the pattern of the tides on their home beach. But after fifteen days, their rhythm had changed. They now opened when the moon, which controls the tides, reached its highest point over their new location, behaving exactly as if the sea's tides were washing in and out over their environment. Scientists guessed it could be because oysters can feel subtle changes in atmospheric pressure caused by the moon's gravitational pull.

Oysters are in harmony with the rhythm of the tides and the moon, opening at high tide and closing at low.

Our bodies, which in an average adult carry about 30 pints of salt water overall, are also influenced by the tides. When the tide is full, we experience the pull; quite literally, we are a little lighter. When the tide is out, we are heavier.

The moon, which controls oysters and humans and the tides of the ocean, was born of the Earth itself, torn from its side when the Earth was young and consisted of a great ball of fire. As it hurtled through space, the Earth developed its own tides, not of the ocean – for there was no water upon the surface of the planet in those distant aeons – but of molten magma. With no land masses to hold them in check those tides rose higher and higher, forming a tsunami of monstrous height such as the world has never known since, nor will ever know again (see page 67–75). Growing far beyond the reach of gravity this cosmic

tsunami tore itself off to shoot out into space. But the Earth's own gravitational field managed to hold on to it just before it hurtled out of reach. And there the moon circles, not so much a satellite as an obedient, silvery child, at peace after its violent birth. The place from which it was torn became the Pacific Ocean.

Greek navigator Pytheas observed and explored unfamiliar high tides in the third century BC when he left the tideless, almost landlocked Mediterranean Sea to explore Britain and beyond; but none of his fellow countrymen believed him on his return – and he himself had no idea that it was the moon which controlled the tides. When Julius Caesar, who had also been born and brought up in the tideless Mediterranean, arrived on the Kentish coast to invade England he wasn't to know that he had arrived at the peak of a 20-foot spring tide with a strong following wind. He moored his ships while he and his men departed to make a reconnaissance; when they returned it was at low tide and they were shocked to find that the entire fleet was left high and dry. Trapped and under ferocious attack by the ancient Britons, the Romans nearly didn't conquer Britain. It wasn't until Isaac Newton came along centuries later that scientists widely recognized that the moon had any effect on ocean tides.

In fact, tides are a response of the waters of the ocean to the pull of the moon as well as to the more distant sun. The influence of the sun is most noticed when the sun, moon and Earth are directly in line, when the pull of the two heavenly bodies are added together to bring water high on the beaches at spring tides – which have nothing to do with the seasons, but quite literally mean the tide is 'springing up'. Low neap tides are

The moon influences the tides: tides are high when the moon is full, and low when the moon is dark. The pull of the moon also affects us: we are lighter when the moon is full and heavier when it is dark.

when the moon, the sun and the Earth are at right angles to each other, forming the apexes of a triangle, when the pull of sun and moon are opposed.

The moon doesn't just affect one side of the world at a time: an equal and opposite bulge of water occurs on the side of the Earth away from the moon due to centrifugal force. As the Earth spins on its axis, these bulges, known as high tides, usually occur twice a day in any one place. An ebb tide is the opposite – it's when the tide is out. When the tide is high on one side of an ocean, it is low on the opposite side. The moon's 28-day cycle is also felt in the periods of the tides. As the moon rises 50 minutes later each day on average than the day before, so in most places the tide is 50 minutes later than the day before. As the moon waxes and wanes in its cycle, so the height of the tides varies, twice each month when the moon is new and old. And, because there are thirteen full moons a year, so too do the tides follow the pattern of the lunar calendar and not the human one of twelve months.

Tidal rhythms as well as range vary from ocean to ocean. Flood tide and ebb tide succeed each other around the world as night follows day; but there is no rule as to whether there shall be two high tides and two low tides in a day, or even just one, as in the Gulf of Mexico which has a diurnal, or daily, rhythm. The Mayans likened it to the breathing of an earth demon. In the far reaches of the Pacific, Tahiti seems to obey the sun rather than the moon. Its high tides are always at noon and midnight; its low tides at six, morning and evening.

There are a few rare and quite baffling exceptions to these patterns. The tides ebb and flow *fourteen* times a day in the narrow channel between mainland Greece and the island of Euboea. The puzzle literally drove Aristotle crazy. This most logical of men is said to have drowned himself because he couldn't explain it – and even today, scientists are mystified.

The Maelstrom

The action of the tides is a lot more complicated than a simple matter of gravity upon water. The height and strength of tides are influenced by many physical things: the difference in distance of Earth to sun and each to the moon; the position of each, north or south of the Equator; the size and depth of their ocean basins, islands and local topography.

Some offshore areas are notoriously dangerous. Often, they are narrow straits between islands – as in Euboea – or bays of a certain shape that seems to funnel the tides in. In Scotland, such areas are known as 'roosts'. The *British Islands Pilot* warns mariners about the roost off Sumburgh Head at the southernmost tip of the Shetland Isles. 'In this confused, tumbling and bursting sea, vessels often become entirely unmanageable and sometimes founder, while others have been tossed about for days together.'

Another warning is given in the *North Sea Pilot* to all shipping regarding the Pentland Firth roost, where the seas are so wild and savage, the incoming tides and the outgoing tides so powerful, that when the tide crosses, or is in opposition to winds, ships can scarcely make headway. Indeed, the roosts, at opposite ends of the Firth, are opposite in behaviour – when one is violent, the other is sweet – and have even been given names: the Bore of Duncansby and the Merry Men of Mey. The Bore of Duncansby is worst on a high tide with an east wind against it, while the Merry Men do the highland fling on an ebb tide against a westerly swell.

'Before entering the Pentland Firth all vessels should be prepared to batten down, and the hatches of small vessels ought to be secured even in the finest weather, as it is difficult to see what may be going on in the distance, and the transition from smooth water to a broken sea is so sudden that no time is given for making arrangements,' the *Pilot* advises, concluding: 'a sea is raised which cannot be imagined by those who have never experienced it.'

It is sadly ironic that Sir James Lighthill, a mathematician and oceanographer who was a leading researcher into wave movements and who was referred to by his fellow scientists as 'a genius', should die while swimming around the Channel island of Sark. In 1973 Sir James became the first person to swim nine miles around the island through dangerous cross currents and tides, by using his knowledge of fluid dynamics to calculate the best route. At the time, he described it as 'a most pleasant way to see the scenery'. He died in 1998, trying to repeat the feat for the sixth time, at the age of seventy-four, in rough seas. A Guernsey police inspector said, 'The tides are pretty big around Sark and there are some ferocious currents.'

Many famous turbulent waters are far more dangerous than the roosts of Scotland. The oldest ones known were the legendary whirlpools of Charybdis in the Strait of Messina which separates Italy and Sicily, scene of some of the terrors described in Homer's classic, the *Odyssey*. They were caused by tides which dashed in from opposite ends of the strait, to meet in the middle with a savage roar that could be heard miles away. In 1908 an earthquake rearranged the sea bed and to some extent tamed the whirlpools.

The Maelstrom was infamous as a place that sank Viking ships long before Edgar

Clinging to the wreckage: famed illustrator Arthur Rackham uses his imagination to illustrate what it must be like to be sucked into a whirlpool, as described by Edgar Allen Poe in his horrifying story 'A Descent into the Maelstrom'.

Allen Poe used it in one of his most chilling stories, 'A Descent into the Maelstrom'. It is near Bodo, some 35 miles north of the Arctic Circle off Norway's northwest coast; but in the same area are so many of the powerful, conflicting currents which are a basic cause of whirlpools that far more dramatic ones may be found. A tortuous stretch of water, the Saltstraumen, connects two fjords. At every change of tide, water surges through this narrow channel with a roar that can be heard miles away. Seen from the beach, the water in the whirlpool created here actually seems to bulge upwards and forms a curve against the sky.

But listen to Poe's description of the account related to him by an old sailor as they crouched on cliffs above the actual maelstrom. According to the sailor, the fishing in those waters was safe in the brief period of slack water between the changes of the tide. He and his three brothers had gone fishing as usual but his watch had stopped. They lost track of time, Too late, as a storm brewed, they realized the tide was surging in and the maelstrom had re-formed, with the winds of the storm lending it epic proportions. Clinging to the sides of their boat, they were relentlessly sucked into the whirlpool.

'Never shall I forget the sensations of awe, horror, and admiration with which I gazed about me. The boat appeared to be hanging, as if by magic, midway down, upon the interior surface of a funnel vast in circumference, prodigious in depth, and whose perfectly smooth sides might have been mistaken for ebony but for the bewildering rapidity with which they spun around, and for the gleaming and ghastly radiance they shot forth, as the rays of the full moon... streamed in a flood of golden glory along the black walls, and far away down into the inmost recesses of the abyss.'

The fisherman went on to describe how he suddenly grew icy cold in resolve and, seeing a barrel spinning by, he remembered that the only whole things washed up on nearby beaches were barrels and casks, because of their shape. At once, he grabbed hold of it and leaped out of the boat, which was dashed to pieces on the rocks at the bottom. Attached to the barrel, he was also sucked into the bottom of the vortex – but, unlike his brothers, survived.

Of course, one can read into this an old seadog's shaggy tale told to a credulous tourist; but whirlpools do exist and all of them – including the maelstrom – can be quite dangerous. More modest, but nonetheless dangerous, whirlpools known as Old Sow also exist in the Bay of Fundy, on the northeastern coast between North America and Canada, where the highest tides on Earth occur.

The Baby's Bath Effect

There is no drop of water in the ocean that does not respond to the mysterious forces that create the tides. The masses of water affected by the tidal movement are enormous. Into Passamaquoddy Bay, just one small inlet in the larger Bay of Fundy, some two billion tons of water are carried by the tidal currents twice each day. Into the whole Bay of Fundy, the amount of water is an incredible 100 billion tons – so heavy that Nova Scotia actually tilts under the load.

Here, the extreme range between high and low tides is as much as 57 feet. What is it about this particular coast that causes these extremes?

The magnetic force of the Earth attracts its own waters with a force millions of times greater than that of the moon and sun. Yet the cosmic pull draws the ocean waters into a pile known as a wave, which in the open sea follows beneath the revolving moon. This is the tidal or moon wave, quite a different thing from the so-called tidal tsunami waves caused by geologic or seismic disturbances on the sea bed (see page 67–75).

The length of a moon wave must be measured in hours rather than distance. It is about 12 hours 20 minutes long – just half the time it takes for the moon to circle the Earth. For each wave on the side of the Earth nearest the moon is balanced by another on the opposite side. The height of the wave is known as the tidal range. In the mid-ocean, the moon wave is about 3 feet high and travels at about 500 miles an hour (the same speed as a tsunami).

Across the shallows of continental shelves and in enclosed seas the tidal wave is slowed down by friction; and as it slows it deepens. Added to this is tidal oscillation – the rocking bowl effect.

If you fill a baby's oval bath with water and gently rock it, waves slop up and down at opposite ends of the bowl – but the part in the middle is relatively calm. This is what happens on a far larger scale in the ocean; the water rocking back and forth is the tide – and, unlike ocean currents or waves, which transmit *energy*, in tides the entire quantity of water in the ocean moves back, and then forth. All bodies of water, natural or artificial, have their own period of oscillation, set in motion by the pull of the sun and the moon. The period is determined by the length and the depth of the sea or lake basin: for example, change the baby's bath for a full-size tub.

This explains the local difference in range; somewhere in the centre of the bowl – the node – is the centre of that baby's bath, where there is relatively little movement. Nantucket is located near the node of its basin and it experiences a low tidal range. On

At low tide in the Bay of Fundy these fishing boats are left high and dry – but at high tide the water can rise an incredible 57 feet.

the other hand, the Bay of Fundy's period of oscillation – actually within the Bay itself – is twelve hours. This very nearly coincides with the period of the tide surging in from the ocean, which is twelve and a half hours.

What happens is that the ocean's tidal waters coincide with, and double up on, the Bay of Fundy's own waters, enormously increasing the strength and height of the tide. This is exaggerated by the shape of the bay in its upper reaches, which is also shallower close to shore. Huge masses of water are crammed into a constantly diminishing area, and the results are the world's highest tides. At Wolfville on the southern shore of Minas Basin, the small harbour is literally empty at low tide. A few hours later up to 57 feet of water surges in.

The most remarkable view of the tide's power in the Bay of Fundy is at Cape Split, on the southern entrance to Minas Basin. The incoming mid-tide roars over a submarine ridge into a narrow deep channel with 'the voice of the moon', that echoes off the towering cliffs and through the pine forest above. With currents in excess of 4 miles an hour, the flow equals the combined flow of all the streams and rivers of the world. Three hours later, the mass of water begins to rush in the opposite direction. Also in the Bay of Fundy are a tidal bore in the Shubenacadie River, a phenomenon that occurs when a strong incoming tide pushes against river water flowing in the opposite direction; the whirlpool known as Old Sow – which seems to generate lots of little swirling piglets (the time for real concern is when the piglets all join up with their mother, forming a giant whirlpool 100 feet across); and 'reversing falls' – which strictly speaking are not falls at all.

As the sea falls a rip tide races out from Cobscook Bay through a narrow funnel that acts like a stopper in a bottle. This blocks the passage of water so that it appears to fall from a height as it empties. Because there are two tides, the second tide comes in before the water from Cobscook Bay has finished emptying, causing dangerous turbulence that has swamped many fishing boats over the years. The most deadly tides occurred in 1869, when the so-called Saxby Gale (named after Lt Saxby of the Royal Navy who predicted it and sent two warnings to the London *Standard*) surged into the Bay of Fundy, killing seventy-one people.

Moon Power

A waterfall 10,000 feet high sounds unbelievable – but this, with one of the greatest tides on earth, occurred six million years ago, between the Mediterranean Sea and the Atlantic Ocean. Today, we know this as the Pillars of Hercules, or the Straits of Gibraltar; but long ago, catastrophic earth movements closed the gap, isolating the Mediterranean. Long ages passed. Despite the inflow of water from great rivers such as the Rhine, the Danube and the Nile, it wasn't enough to compete with the power of the sun. Over the course of just 1,000 years, the Mediterranean evaporated and its floor turned into a 2000-mile long desert of arid salt pans and salt lakes – 10,000 feet below its neighbouring ocean, the Atlantic.

Perhaps there was an earthquake, perhaps there was a giant storm-surge coupled with an extra-high spring tide; whatever the reason, a million and a half years later, the

Atlantic suddenly burst through the Straits and its waters poured down into the empty basin so many thousands of feet below, making a waterfall of truly awesome proportions. The great surge of water that flooded across the empty plain to refill the Mediterranean was equally gigantic.

All of this came to light when the US research ship, the *Gomar Challenger*, carried out geological drillings in the bottom of the Mediterranean, producing some very puzzling findings. Hundreds of feet below the current floor of the Mediterranean, scientists found gravel beds and then a layer of evaporites – rock formed from the ancient salt desert. With other strong evidence, the *Challenger* team was able to put together the story of the prehistoric waterfall. Less awesome but still spectacular waterfalls, such as Niagara, have been harnessed in recent times to produce electricity. The tides too could be used – a single 4-foot wave advancing along a 100-foot front would produce enough electricity to light an average city for 24 hours. It's safe and environmentally sound – but it's a source of power that has been little used in modern times. Medieval man, while not having the technology to harness waterfalls, did use the power of tides to grind flour.

The only surviving tide mill in the world was built at Totton, near Southampton, England, in the thirteenth century. Reconstructed in 1785, it is still in use. It operates by means of a causeway that blocks the tidal Bartley estuary to create a tide pool, which is filled twice a day by Southampton's unusual double high tide – which has a range of about 12 feet. Enough energy is stored in the mill pond to allow the wheel to still grind wheat for about seven and a half hours. Similar tide mills were in common use up and down the European seaboard from earliest times, while one was in regular use from as far back as 1640 at the mouth of the North River in Salem, Massachusetts. With the steam age, the free source of tidal power fell out of fashion.

Today, enormous projects to make electricity from sea power have been constructed or are under construction. The Rance estuary barrage near St Malo in Brittany, operational since 1982, uses sluice gates to trap the 44-foot incoming tide. Twice a day, one of the highest tides in the world surges up the estuary and back, reaching a maximum volume of about 280 million gallons a minute. Despite fears, the environment has not been damaged; the estuary above the dam has not silted up – although an unexpected side effect, according to scientists, is that the braking effect on the tide has imperceptibly slowed the rate of rotation of the earth, something which the tides do anyway. Tidal friction has caused the day to lengthen by one second every 100,000 years or so. If the sun doesn't incinerate the Earth first, there will come a day that is as long as the lunar month would eventually be – approximately forty days long. It is not known how many such tidal stations it would take to make a difference – if any – to the rotation of the Earth, but many more are planned for the future.

In Scotland, two prototype wave energy plants are being tested: an underground one on the Isle of Islay that does not spoil the scenery; and the other known as Salters' ducks, which operates on a system of hollow, oscillating floats or ducks made of concrete. Earlier, in the USA, both presidents Roosevelt and Kennedy were convinced that the enormous power rushing into the Bay of Fundy should be harnessed. A few

months before his death, Kennedy said: 'I think this can be one of the most astonishing and beneficial joint enterprises that the people of the US could undertake.' The project has been implemented with a small tidal power plant in the Annapolis Basin, which nevertheless generates about 1 per cent of Nova Scotia's electricity. Large-scale plants have been delayed, not only because of the incredible cost, but because of protests by environmentalists.

Electricity from tide power: the sea entering through sluices in the Rance river barrage at St Malo, France, drives turbines in an ecologically sound way.

One other phenomenon of the Mediterranean, caused by the ancient geological structure at the Pillars of Hercules, is that often the Atlantic and the Mediterranean are at different levels – quite remarkable for two bodies of water that are actually touching.

About 150 fathoms below the Straits of Gibraltar is an underwater sill, an ancient geological structure that once was a lip of the giant waterfall. Here, on the surface, the deep Mediterranean spills over its rocky edge into the open waters of the Atlantic because of the conditions that prevail in the Mediterranean, where the hot sun beating down on its nearly enclosed water creates an extremely high rate of evaporation. More water is drawn into the atmosphere than enters from its rivers – exactly as happened millions of years ago. The water becomes saltier and more dense, until the surface of the Mediterranean falls below that of the Atlantic. At a certain point, lighter, less salty water from the Atlantic pours past Gibraltar almost like a powerful river entering the Mediterranean.

In past centuries while this happened, sailing ships were stuck, often for months on end: one captain wrote in his log: 'I have been weather bound for six weeks. Got as far as Malaga, only to be swept back by the current. Indeed no vessel has been able to get out into the Atlantic for three months past.'

The powerful surface currents flowing into the Mediterranean do so at an average

rate of three knots; but an unsuspected bottom current moving into the Atlantic is even stronger. It is so vigorous that it has been known to wreck oceanographic instruments used to measure it.

The Roar of the Black Dragon

When Victor Hugo's favourite daughter, Léopoldine, died in 1843 at the age of just nineteen, he was so heartbroken that his intense grief could only find shape in two volumes of poems. It was to be many years before he attempted writing a novel again – the masterpiece he then achieved was *Les Misérables*. Bizarrely, Léopoldine and her new husband drowned in a boating accident on the River Seine – their boat overturned by an unexpectedly large bore, pushed many miles further upstream by higher tides and winds in the Channel than normal.

Major bores form only in a few rivers around the world, where there are large and rapid changes in water volume. The mouth or estuary has to be shallow, narrowing quickly into a V-shaped river, like a funnel, so the incoming tide is literally 'funnelled in' to push against the outgoing fresh water of the river. The tide level increases more

rapidly than the tide wave can move so it forms a kind of surging wall of water, a turbulent wave front that roars in from the sea with a perceptible noise that can often be heard for many miles. It is the noise as much as the power of the water that has traditionally terrified primitive people, who have given the bores various demonic names and attributes.

In China, one of the most dramatic bores in the world is named the Black Dragon, a contradiction in many respects because to the Chinese dragons are a potent symbol of good fortune – while black is the colour of disaster and danger. But the Chinese, more than most, understand conflict and harmony, ebb and flow. Where the Qiantang River meets with the South China Sea, in the province of Zhejiang, the people live between the land and the sea. Just as the tides are subject to the moon and the sun, so their lives are subject to the tides. For thousands of years, they have sought to live in harmony with the twice-daily influx of the Black Dragon.

In this prosperous region of China, the farmers depend on the Qiantang for food, for fresh drinking water and for irrigation. But their livelihoods – indeed, their lives – are at constant risk because the daily tidal surge, the bore, that daily rips up their river is the fiercest in the world. The fishermen who work here have learned to ride the bore, working with it and not against it, because they must fish to earn a living; so every day they gamble their boats and their lives – it's the power of the Black Dragon against their skill. They don't always win.

Earlier generations erected pagodas along the riverbank to try to pacify the waters. One king even had 10,000 archers fire arrows into the waves in a hopeless attempt to subdue them. In the Temple of the Ocean God, prayers are offered even today to ward off disaster. In the face of the Black Dragon, the fishermen take no chances, because the fishing is good.

Fisherman and boat owner Gao Zhi Xiang explains: 'When we see the tide coming good and strong, we get back to shore fast. By the time it gets here, we are already on dry land. We've lived by the water all our lives. We raise the boat when we see the water's getting higher than the day before, hoisting the boats up high when the tide hits hard.'

You hear the tide long before you see it: the weight of the oncoming ocean churns rocks and boulders along the sea bed with the roar of a dragon, or the sound of battle drums; the white crests skipping along the wall of water give little idea of the force behind them. When the water comes closer, it is a wonderful, frothy caramel colour; the Black Dragon looks more like a fierce lion with a magnificent mane.

Here it is shown in one of its less furious moods, but, when deadly, the flow of China's famed Black Dragon bore is five times that of Niagara Falls as it surges into the Qiantang River mouth. You can hear the bore long before you see it as waves up to 30-feet high churn rocks and boulders along in a frothy caramel-brown mêlée.

For fishermen with larger boats the tidal surge is a real threat – but it's also an opportunity because the weight of water is pushing fish from the deep ocean straight to their nets. Shi, owner of one of the boats, explains why they run such risks: 'There are more fish when the tide is big. When the tide is still growing, the fish come in shoals; and when the tide arrives it brings the fish to the surface so it is easier to catch them in the net.'

Often, the fishing boats are caught out at sea, in the mesh of the tide. The surge of water goes across the entire river mouth, a distance of some 6 miles from shore to shore without a break. The fishermen's only choice is to take the oncoming waves head on: to ride the Dragon.

For generations people have tried to tame China's Black Dragon bore. One king even ordered 10,000 archers to fire arrows into the waves in an attempt to 'kill' them. Today, this symbolic archer can still be found near a temple on the banks of the Qiantang River.

Gao Zhi Xiang says: 'We call it "Man fighting the Tide". To survive, man must fight the tide. You must concentrate. You can't take it lightly. It can kill you if you get it wrong. When I shot the tide for the first time I was very nervous. My heart beat very fast. It would be better if there was no tide at all, but we can't do a thing about it. That's nature.'

It is nature at war with itself. As the tide roars on up the river, it's as if the ocean is invading the land. Its boiling fury has only one release – to turn back on itself towards the open sea. The ancient Chinese said it was like the charge of a mighty army that no one could withstand.

For one young man who watches the tides for a living, the twice-daily battle is a fascinating, though lonely, one. Zhou Ke Gang is just twenty-two years old and has a heavy responsibility. In a reinforced concrete blockhouse perched on an island, he carries out his duties as keeper of the tidal station. His job is to monitor the current and measure the salt content in the water.

The fierce flow of the Qiantang has carried millions of tons of sand and silt on a 500-mile journey, all the way from the Yellow River down to the South China Sea. When the ocean spills ashore it's the sandbars across the river mouth that trigger this particular tidal surge – a surge of such force that it reverses the river's flow for some 20 miles upstream.

Zhou Ke Gang says: 'The tide is like a rule. It comes in twice a day from the ocean, from the Bohai Gulf... forming a tidal bore. The mouth of the river is shaped like a trumpet. When the tide comes in, it's spectacular. Small boats try to get to the bank before the tide arrives because it's dangerous. Many small boats have been turned over and lots of people killed.'

The flow of the Black Dragon is five times that of the Niagara Falls. It is also deadly. In the autumn of 1993, eighty-seven people who had come to watch were killed by it, swept away from under their feet or in their cars by the sheer force. In the eighteenth century, whipped up by gale-force winds, it wiped out over 10,000 people inhabiting its fertile shores. Defence walls built to protect the rich farming land frequently collapse when weather and tide conditions add to the bore's strength. No one has ever surfed the Black Dragon, although British surfer Stuart Mathews tried – and lasted for just ten seconds. If he had realized that behind the wall of water he was trying to ride was an entire ocean of unstoppable water, he might have paused to think.

Major bores, while not common, are found elsewhere in the world where the coastal topography is right. One very alarming one is at Broadsounds Bay in Queensland, Australia, where there is a wide estuary mouth with many sandbanks, giving way to a rapidly narrowing river. Here the tide seems to instantly change direction – and when it rushes in, it is often laden with fish trapped by the surge. Following closely behind them are dozens of sharks which are sometimes swept miles upstream to where the river is really quite narrow and small. Swimmers and sailboat owners are often unexpectedly confronted with a wall of water filled with snapping jaws which are quite happy to catch people instead of fast-moving, more evasive fish. Over the years there have been many fatalities.

The Amazon bore is quite unexpected, given that the power of the Amazon river is such that its enormous current of water is swept many hundreds of miles out to sea (in fact, due to the outgoing strength of the river, offshore the sea is fresh, not salt). But the energy of the bore here is not deep; it's a surface current that is born when incoming tides surge up over a shelf of mud dumped in the river mouth from the outward flow of the river, carrying vast quantities of mud from the rainforests. Similarly, in India and Pakistan, the Indus and the Hoogly Rivers also have tidal bores formed because of extensive sandbanks that act as a shelf to push the sea into a funnel. In the busy port of Calcutta on the Hoogly, ocean-going shipping has to take special precautions to prevent being capsized. Pilots come out to guide shipping in, following a careful path marked out by buoys.

Sometimes a bore is so powerful that it backs up the actual river water, pushing it far inland. The River Severn in Bristol is probably the best-known bore in Europe, and one that is very dangerous to shipping and small boats crossing its path. In medieval times, before weirs controlled the river, a swordfish was caught far upstream in Worcester and is still a point of interest in the town.

WAVES

A nightmare scenario for a captain on the bridge of an ocean liner is suddenly to see a wall of water 100 feet high, filling the sky from horizon to horizon, bearing down on his vessel at something approaching 50 miles an hour. He does what he can: he turns the bow into the wave to present the least possible target and prevent his ship breaching. Then, to his horror, just before the wave hits, he realizes that a trough, almost as deep as the wave is high, lurks at the base of the wave – and his ship is about to tip over the edge to ski helplessly down the slope, down and down, plummeting to the very depths of the ocean. Even if there were any chance that the ship could somehow rise to the surface from this terrible hole in the sea, the thousands of tons of ominous green water looming so far above, ready to crash down with unimaginable force, would ensure that the ship and its crew would vanish – wiped off the face of the ocean to become yet another unexplained mystery.

Ever since the days of the Phoenicians, waves which mysteriously swallowed ships have terrified mariners. For centuries monstrous waves of unimaginable height, described by sailors who survived them, were dismissed as yet another mariner's salty tale – along with sea serpents and mermaids. In fact, few ships do survive the truly giant waves of the sea, so eyewitness accounts have always been rare.

When French scientist and naval officer Captain Dumont d'Urville, in charge of a maritime expedition in 1826, reported waves 80 to 100 feet high, he was mocked by the establishment and his position as a scientist thrown into jeopardy – even though three of his colleagues confirmed his sightings.

But among all the waves of the sea, what are these strangely terrifying things that have caused and still cause so much havoc?

Giant ocean waves formed by the wind are known by a number of names, but more familiarly are described as freak or rogue. They are neither tidal waves nor tsunamis: the latter, known incorrectly as tidal waves, are caused by undersea earthquakes or volcanic eruptions, the effects of which have devastated entire coastal communities for thousands of years (see page 86–87).

The one thing that establishes a freak wave as being different from just a big wave is its extreme height and the extreme depth of its trough.

No one knows exactly how many ships have been sunk by freak waves. Lloyd's of

A rare photograph of the face of a freak wave over 60 feet high about to engulf the *British Wye* during a North Atlantic storm off Newfoundland. The tanker survived, but with considerable damage.

London, the world's leading marine insurance underwriter, reports that in the past decade an average of forty-six ships a year of over 500 tons were simply overpowered by the sea. Some undoubtedly succumbed to normal storm seas – a large wave doesn't have to be rogue to be destructive. But rogue waves may be responsible for a high proportion of these losses.

Sometimes there is a brief cry for help. In 1986 the Cypriot tanker *Cretan Star* disappeared in the Indian Ocean some 400 miles southwest of Bombay – leaving only an oil slick. A panic-stricken radio message moments before reported that she had been hit by a huge wave – then silence. A 'wall of water' reared up and sank a sportfishing boat,

Morning Cloud, former prime minister Edward Heath's racing yacht, seen here with billowing sails off Cowes, Isle of Wight, on a breezy day, disappeared mysteriously in 1989 in the same waters, possibly sunk by a freak wave.

Fish-n-Fool, off Baja, California, claiming ten lives. But other ships disappear without a last message, leaving no trace. In 1976 the Panamanian tanker *Grand Zenith* disappeared in a storm off Nova Scotia. In 1974 the *Gaul*, a Hull trawler with every modern navigation and communication aid, vanished in Arctic waters with no warning, no clues, taking her entire crew of thirty-six men with her. In 1989 *Morning Cloud*, former British prime minister Edward Heath's yacht, sank in equally strange silence in the English Channel. The discovery of the *Gaul* in August 1998, with her hatches open and lying in 300 metres in the Barents Sea, has only served to deepen the mystery.

Every sea, every latitude, claims ships of every type and size as if they have been plucked from the ocean – but only relatively recently in the long history of navigation has the likely cause been acknowledged.

The First Confirmed Freak Wave

It wasn't until 1933 when Lieutenant E. C. Margraff, watch officer – and thus a qualified naval observer – on a navy tanker, the USS *Ramapo*, confirmed that he had seen and accurately measured by triangulation a wave 112 feet high during a terrible seven-day storm in the North Pacific, that freak waves started to be taken seriously by scientists. Even then, many of them doubted the observer's measurements and demanded that the mathematics be re-examined. Fortunately, Lt Margraff had logged his report meticulously, giving precise figures, also recording that the winds were 70 knots directly astern, chased by mountainous seas when he measured the wave. So, with the likelihood that the figures were accurate, reports of other sightings and the devastating effect of monster waves moved out of the realm of tall stories and into the realm of science.

From then on, freak wave events were reported with more confidence by witnesses; no longer was there a conspiracy of silence among ships' crews who – like Captain d'Urville – were wary of being ridiculed. Stories began to be reported in the press. In the winter of 1942 one of the worst naval disasters in history was narrowly averted when the luxury liner *Queen Mary* – at that time requisitioned as a troop carrier, with nearly 15,000 American troops heading for the battlefields of Europe – encountered a freak wave south of Newfoundland, the graveyard of many ships. According to London's *Daily Mail*, the great liner was weathering a North Atlantic gale, labouring through heavy seas, when a massive wave slammed into her broadside on. In seconds – too fast for lifeboat drill or for boats to be launched – the ship had rolled over on her side and men and equipment slid helplessly down a near-vertical slope. Her upper decks – normally high above the sea – were awash and it seemed that she would capsize. For moments she hung in the balance, just 5 degrees away from the point of no return, until with painful slowness she righted herself. Three people were killed and hundreds injured in this near-catastrophe.

Every ship has a degree of roll beyond which there is no recovery. Two forces are involved in the fight for stability: the downward push of gravity – with the combined weight of the vessel, contents and passengers all seeking the gravitational centre of the Earth – and the upward lift of buoyancy, the force of all the air inside the hull trying to rise above the water level, keeping it afloat. In a well-made ship sailing on a calm sea, the two forces are equal and cancel each other out along the centreline. But when a ship is breached and gets shoved on to her side by waves, the two forces are laterally opposed and the centre of buoyancy shifts to the submerged side where more air is forced below the waterline. Normally, the two forces work against each other and the ship rights herself on to an even keel; but the more the ship 'falls over' to lie on her side the further apart the two opposing forces are – until a stage is reached where gravitation wins the battle. The lateral distance between the two forces is called the righting arm; and the torque they generate is the righting moment. The taller the ship, the more likely she is to capsize. In the case of the *Queen Mary*, the design of the vessel meant that the righting moment and buoyancy won; but often in the combat with a killer wave, the sheer weight and downward force of water taken aboard – downflooding – is too much and the ship is lost with all hands. Some ships, especially steel-hulled ones that don't have the benefit of the buoyancy of wood, can sink so rapidly they look as if they have been yanked from below by a giant hand. Even if the crew manage to jump overboard in an attempt to swim away, the vacuum caused as the ship goes down at such an incredible speed drags them down with it.

Half a century later another 'queen', the *Queen Elizabeth II*, encountered a similar freak wave in the same seas, but her modern stabilizers ensured that she pulled through. Captain Ronald Warwick was later seen on television, reporting that he was standing on the bridge when he saw a massive wave looming ahead with the typical straight horizon line of all such waves. He said it looked as if the ship were sailing directly for the white cliffs of Dover – adding that when the wave hit and flooded the bridge, 90 feet above the sea, he felt as if they had collided with a solid wall.

Once the metaphorical flood-gates were opened and freak waves became widely accepted, it wasn't long before scientists – the very same people who had previously

The luxury liner *Queen Mary* refitted for war service with nearly 15,000 US troops crowded aboard destined for the battlefields of Europe in 1942. Nearly breached by an extreme storm wave in a North Atlantic gale, she managed to right herself – narrowly averting what would have been one of the worst naval disasters in history.

denied their existence – started work in earnest, analysing and interpreting the sightings and experiences to quantify exactly what a freak wave was. To the surprise of many, it was discovered that there were at least nine types of abnormal waves – eleven if tidal bores and tsunamis were included – whose origins were as complicated as they were numerous. The following list summarizes the various types of what are formally called Extreme Storm Waves (ESWs). ESWs can occur as single huge waves or, more often, in groups – normally of three, when they are called 'three-sisters' waves.

▶ **Hurricane and typhoon ESWs**

Generally, waves whipped up by the wind, fed by thunderstorms, downbursts, typhoons, hurricanes and tornadoes. Their complex wind field is circular, with about a 15-degree inward slope that increases in strength towards the eye wall, in turn pushing wave trains into a central mixing pot, where they achieve truly awesome proportions. Often many different systems go into the feeder bands of these storms, making them erratic in speed and course. (See Chapter 2.)

▶ **Meteorological bomb ESWs**

The winter equivalent of a hurricane, where the central pressure drops 24 millibars in 24 hours. In simplistic terms, a cold and violent downdraught hits the sea at an angle and pushes up a wall of water. The air temperature of these

View from a helicopter: damage to the USS *Valley Forge* after being hit by a freak wave. Clearly seen, a sizeable piece of the flight deck – made of steel with 6 inches of laminated teak wood bolted on to it – has been torn away. Some of it is still hanging precariously, while other large sections have fallen into the sea. Under this deck are rooms, essentially a steel honeycomb made to absorb bomb damage.

storms is often much colder than the ocean, generating much turbulence as the cold air drops very fast with rapidly increasing downward winds, which gain more 'bite' on the surface of the sea, shoving up massive waves.

► POLAR LOW ESWs

Similar to meteorological bomb ESWs in that they are developed out of large winter cold fronts moving in rapidly from a direction that is usually west of the storm centre, which contains wind speed surge lines and squall lines. There is an extremely confused pattern, with wind shifts and gusts pushing the squall line along, showers and often thunderstorms as heavy cold air replaces warm air on the ocean surface, whipping up the waves and sending great clouds surging upwards to meet cold air again at a high level – which is where the rain and the hail associated with these storms develop. One common element is the sudden, extreme cold with massive waves that seem to come from every direction.

► DOWNBURST ESWs

Again, similar to meteorological bomb and polar low ESWs; but caused almost exclusively by thunderstorms moving at the group velocity of wave trains. The pressure changes involved in a long run of downbursts and heavy rain storms over the sea associated with thunderstorms in tandem with the waves build them up to unusual heights. (See Chapter 2.)

▶ **CROSSING WAVE TRAINS**

Also known as wind-current interactions. Generally caused by refraction or reflection of deep water waves, which leads to the path of wave trains crossing. Waves nearly equal to the combined height of the waves that make up the train may develop leading to often quite rough seas. This is noticeable around small islands, where two currents divide and then come together either normally or in a more exaggerated way as the result of a storm – which demonstrates why ships should be careful when seeking shelter from a severe storm in the lee of an island. Similar results occur on shallow submarine banks and bars.

▶ **SHOALING FREAK WAVES**

These occur when storm-driven waves on one side of the ocean travel thousands of miles across the depths, growing in size until they arrive at the continental shelf on the other side, where the bottom of the sea rises quite steeply. These steep-faced waves feel bottom, are compressed, and rear up, forming massive breakers. Among areas where they are experienced are the Bay of Biscay, the west coasts of Ireland and Scotland and the northern coasts of Hawaii.

▶ **CURRENT FREAK WAVES**

Also known as random reinforcements of wave trains. When a current over 4 knots is opposed by wave trains, the waves increase by as much as twice the height of waves outside the current. In certain circumstances, this can be factored proportionately upwards into waves four times the height of waves outside the current. Some examples of this can be seen in the Agulhas Current off South Africa and the Kuroshio Current off Japan where even super-tankers can be destroyed. Another area notorious for such waves is the Gulf Stream which has a current of 4 knots. When a Noreaster storm occurs exactly over the Gulf Stream, current freak waves of 80 feet are encountered.

▶ **LANDSLIDE AND GLACIER FREAK WAVES**

If a landslide occurs in a constricted place, such as a bay, or a glacier breaks off and falls into an inlet, the waves generated can reach monstrous proportions – the highest in the world. When 90 million tons of rock and ice broke off from a 3,000-foot-high glacier and plunged into Lituya Bay, Alaska, the wave raised scoured the mountain on the opposite side of the bay clean of all trees and vegetation – even earth – to a height of 1,720 feet.

Nautical Wave Scale

This is a widely accepted code of wave states.

Code	Description	Max. height of wave (in feet)
0	glassy calm	0
1	calm (ripples)	0–1
2	smooth wavelets	1–2
3	slight	2–4
4	moderate	4–8
5	rough	8–13
6	very rough	13–20
7	high	20–30
8	very high	30–45
9	phenomenal, tremulous (i.e. unable to sustain own weight and collapsing)	over 45

Surf surging high up a sandy beach on an island at the start of a tropical storm.

► HURRICANE STORM SURGE

Usually caused by offshore tropical cyclones, these destructive waves are often erroneously called tidal waves. Normally, wind moves waves at low to moderate speeds; but a hurricane or cyclone, with incredibly high wind speed, can literally 'shovel' the water along until it approaches a shore, when the rising shoal causes the water to spring up. The water piles up vertically into a mound – the storm surge. As it moves inland, it makes a base for other waves to ride piggy-back on it, sometimes as much as a mile inland.

Storm surge height is measured in still water: that is, the height of the mound of water without waves, both of which relate to the speed of the wind exponentially. For example, a category 1 hurricane (on the Saffir/Simpson Hurricane Scale) has winds of 74–95 miles an hour and a storm surge of 4–5 feet. Category 4 has winds of 131–55 miles an hour and a storm surge of 13–18 feet. (See Chapter 2.)

► SOLITONS

Solitary waves which do not travel in wave trains with a specific periodicity and appear from nowhere. They have two forms: surface waves and internal waves, with a pulse waveform. They were first described in the west by skippers of tea clippers sailing through the Malacca Straits or the Andaman Sea as 'boiling seas' or 'rip tides' – and scorned by experts who didn't accept their existence. They are formed in shallow bodies of water which are nearly closed in by islands; tidal currents forced between the land and reduced in depth form excited seas with dangerous flurries of high waves which move forward to engulf ships before dissipating. Little wonder that ancient sailors thought they were caused by monsters lurking beneath the waves.

▶ **THE NON-NEGOTIABLE WAVE**
Possibly the most chilling one of all; it simply means that whatever type the wave is, nothing can survive it.

The 100-Fathom Line

Captain T. Wilson Cameron was one of the first to report the curious likelihood of encountering freak waves in the area of the 100-fathom line of a continental shelf, although – as with other sailors who have made similar observations about freak waves – he was at first ignored.

During the storms of January 1961, Captain Cameron, then master of a small coastal ship, was sailing across the notorious Bay of Biscay with the wind on his starboard quarter when he encountered a moderate gale with very rough seas off the northwest

Sunk by extreme storm waves, a ship is washed up in furous surf.

coast of Spain. 'My Spanish third mate, an excellent and mature officer, fixed our position by bearings of shore lights and reported that they were on the 100-fathom line, with the comment: "Very dangerous seas are often found around here." When I asked him where he had obtained this information, the Spaniard said his father and grandfather, who had fished these seas all their lives, had warned him to keep clear of the 100-fathom line.'

An astonishing 100-foot 'wall of water' freak wave encountered by a tanker along the 100-fathom line in the Bay of Biscay. Luckily, this ship saw the wave in time and turned into it. Had it been at night or in bad weather, then such a wave striking a ship abeam would almost certainly have sunk it within moments.

Taking note – and perhaps recalling the song about the infamous storms encountered in the Bay of Biscay – Cameron ordered a change of course four points to starboard and within an hour they were out of the rough seas. 'I have always remembered my shipmate's advice,' recalls Cameron, 'and have passed the information on to the many officers I sailed with afterwards, especially if we were passing the Bay of Biscay.'

Other masters, however, weren't as convinced as Captain Cameron about this. Some years later, he was sailing as chief officer on a very sound 156,000-ton ore carrier, built with bridge amidships and engines aft, on a northerly course laid across the Bay of Biscay. In Admiralty charts there was a printed notice advising shipping to give the coast a wide berth because the cliffs were too high to see warning lights properly – and so it was normal for ships' captains to steer for the 100-fathom line of the continental shelf. Remembering the advice of his former third mate, Cameron warned his captain, who said he didn't believe old wives' tales and directed that they were to stay on the same course.

'A few days later, we were off the northwest coast of Spain, in a north-by-west wind, force 6 to 7, with the ship spraying and occasionally shipping water, but this was not unusual nor alarming. It was night, with the moon partly obscured with clouds, when everything suddenly went dark. I looked to port and was horrified to discover that an immense wave, approaching rapidly on the starboard beam, had entirely blotted out the moon.'

The wave, which was coming from a direction 90 degrees different from the normal sea and wind, was like a vertical wall of water filling the sky from far north to south with no crest or white streaks. Cameron yelled to the lookout man, who was on the opposite side of the bridge, to come into the wheelhouse to see the wave. 'Amazed, we watched as it started to break 80 to 100 yards away. Then it was on us, hitting the ship fair abeam with three distinct shocks, sweeping the vessel her full length. Fortunately, the ship had rolled away just before impact, so the damage was less than it would otherwise have been – even so, some of it was quite extraordinary, indicating a three-sisters wave higher than 85 feet.'

Two floodlights bolted to the bridge were swept away up to the bridge, along with heavy steel ladders which were twisted and jammed into a nearby alleyway; while heavy glass in the bridgehouse itself was cracked. The forecastle head deck was pushed down 3 inches and, inside, 14-inch channel bars were cracked through; 5-inch stanchions were buckled, heavy wooden beams cracked from top to bottom and decking was wrecked; but the ship was still seaworthy.

They were lucky. A few years later, in another January – of 1984 – an Italian bulk carrier, en route from Genoa to Rotterdam, also halfway across the Bay of Biscay on the 100-fathom line, reported that all was well. That was its last message. It was never heard of again, the second ship from the same company that disappeared in the same way at the same place within a year.

So what causes these 100-fathom waves? It is thought that storm-driven deep rollers, coming clear across the Atlantic without interruption, suddenly hit the continental shelf at the 100-fathom line and are compressed, rearing up out of the sea to terrorize shipping. Another theory is that the Bay of Biscay is a place where several tides and currents meet; every now and then normal waves rolling in towards the shore, get into step (see page 62) – thus creating a monster.

Strangely enough, Captain Cameron encountered yet another freak wave, on the other side of the Atlantic.

'In 1963 I was on a newly built bulk carrier sailing out of Texas en route to Rotterdam. We had just passed Miami and were in the axis of the Gulf Stream on a beautiful cloudless night, with barely a ripple on the surface of the sea and a full moon shining above. Suddenly the entire ship lifted forward. I ran to the window and saw an immense white foaming mass

close ahead. I raced to the wheelhouse, arriving there just as the wave crashed on deck. It was a beautiful and dangerous sight, the entire ship alive with white water and foaming phosphorescence. Then the wave was gone – and the surface of the sea once again was calm.'

Very little damage was done, beyond a twisted ladder leading up to the mast house; but while they had been loading in Texas, another ship, the MV *Sulphur Queen*, left just ahead of them on the same track. It vanished. Had it met the full force of the same wave further along the sea lane? On checking, Cameron learned that an intense low had remained stationary for a few days northeast of Cape Hatteras, North Carolina, perfect breeding ground for such an unusual wave. A few years later, Cameron bought a paperback, *The Bermuda Triangle*, which describes mysterious disappearances in that part of the sea. He read that an American passenger ship from Miami to Nassau had encountered a sudden wave at the same time and in the same place and he wondered whether one or more waves from the same system had been shared by all three ships at slightly different intervals.

Also struck by a freak wave off the coast of Bermuda, in 1984, the 117-foot square-rigger *Marques* sank in less than a minute while most of its youthful crew slept below deck.

Shortly before dawn on Sunday 3 June of that year the three-masted sailing ship sailed into a fierce squall about 75 miles north of Bermuda. Heavy rain began to pelt the ship and a furious wind sprang up out of nowhere. Squalls were nothing new to the *Marques*, one of thirty-nine tall ships participating in a transatlantic race. But as a precaution, Stuart Finlay, the experienced American captain of the ship, shortened the sails. The *Marques* was carrying a crew of twenty-eight – half of whom were under twenty-five years of age. At the helm twenty-two-year-old Philip Sefton fought the waves. Suddenly a heavy gust of wind pushed the *Marques* down on its starboard side. At the same instant 'a freakish wave of incredible force and size', as Sefton later described it, slammed the ship broadside, pushing its masts further beneath the surging water. A second wave crashed down on the ship and it filled with water. It sank in less than one minute. Only Sefton and eight shipmates survived. An investigation concluded that the fierce, unexpected wind had undoubtedly contributed to the tragedy, but the fatal blow was delivered by the rogue wave. Possibly the *Marques* was in the wrong place at the wrong time – possibly the wave was not all that large – but it was speculated that most of the wave's energy was concentrated in the wave-cresting front, causing the ship to capsize beyond its righting moment. If the *Marques* had been just 500 feet or so from the spot it might have survived.

From Cat's Paws to Freak Waves

The smallest, newest *normal* waves are called endearingly 'cats' paws'. They are little diamond-shaped capillary ripples on the surface of a glassy sea that do indeed look like a curved cat's paw patting at the water. Weaker than the surface tension in the sea, these little waves fade as soon as the wind dies. But if a blow is about to develop, cats'

The *Marques*, a beautiful square-rigged sailing ship, was sunk by a freak wave off Bermuda during a transatlantic race in 1984, while most of her young crew slept below.

paws give the wind an initial purchase and at winds over 6 knots proper waves start to build. The harder the wind blows, the more friction there is, the bigger the waves get and the more wind they are able to 'catch' – just like the sails of a ship.

Exponentially, wave height rises with wind speed. At this stage, if the wind suddenly stopped, the waves would continue under their own momentum, using the energy developed by falling into their own troughs (the one that precedes them; the trough behind belongs to the wave behind). Such windless waves are called gravity waves, or swells. If a bit of flotsam floats on one of these swells, it remains where it is as the wave passes underneath it, clearly demonstrating the fact that ocean waves are among the Earth's most complicated natural phenomena. They give the appearance of endlessly moving forward, of rolling along over the oceans and seas of the world, of surging in on to the shore; yet, they don't travel at all; or at least, the actual water particles within any individual wave stay in the same position. In other words, although the *energy* of the wave is moving, the *water* within it is not. This is a good thing, because should all the water of all the oceans march forward with the waves the result would be catastrophic. (To a lesser degree we can see just how disastrous when, for a brief moment, water is pushed on land by a tsunami or a massive storm surge.)

The higher the swell, the further apart the crests and the faster their speed. Antarctic storms can have crests half a mile apart travelling at 30 or 40 miles an hour.

By the time they reach Hawaii they are the fluid and beautiful breakers 40 feet high so loved by surfers.

Scientists understand how waves in general work; but they are still largely baffled by the mechanics of the really enormous ones, which seem to exceed the forces generating them. What causes these deadly sea mountains of water? Until recently, oceanographers seemed to agree on a single explanation: rogue waves are the result of a rare coincidence of ordinary wave dynamics; but with more research the science has grown more exact.

Heights of waves relate to how hard the wind blows, how long it blows for and how much open water or sea room – 'the fetch' – there is. '*Speed, duration and fetch*' is the equation. Force 12 winds over a small stretch of water (such as one of the Great Lakes) would generate waves of 35 feet in height after 12 hours or so; but that's about the maximum they can go because they soon run out of 'fetch'. The maximum possible for any given circumstance is known as a 'fully developed sea state'.

Every wind has a minimum duration and fetch to reach a fully developed sea state. If the wind blows at 30 knots over a fetch of 280 nautical miles for at least 23 hours, a fully risen sea will result, with average waves of 13 feet, and the highest wave approaching 30 feet. A gale blowing across a thousand miles of ocean for something like eight or nine days would generate wave heights of 97 feet; and according to the mathematics, peak wave heights would be double that. Waves that height have never been recorded – but they have been observed. We know they are out there – but the trouble is that at the moment most equipment, such as that on weather buoys, only allows for the 100-foot wave to be recorded; anything beyond that usually breaks the equipment.

Freak and storm waves have maths that could scare mariners to death if they paused to think about it. Wave energy doesn't rise linearly with wind speed but multiplies to its fourth power. A 40-knot wind is not twice as violent as a 20-knot wind – it is many times as violent. Waves can very rapidly change from friendly curves to having shorter crests and steeper wave faces, the kind of face that moves like a sheer wall, or forms a near-vertical trough that a ship's bow can plunge into – and keep on going to the bottom of the sea.

If the height of a wave is more than one-seventh the distance between the crests, or the wavelength, the waves cannot support themselves and start to break under their own weight. They also break if they hit a rising shoreline because the underwater turbulence, sand, gravel or rocks, slows the waves down, thus shortening the wavelength and changing the ratio of height to length.

Wave-power

Breaking waves do not just have tremendous force; they also have tremendous weight, far more than the actual weight of water. Instantaneous pressure of up to 6,000 pounds per square foot has been measured; in higher waves the force may be greater. If these breaking waves hit a ship sideways on (as in the case of the *Queen Mary* or the *Marques*) they will succeed in shoving her over and under – and if they

break under the bow or a stern, they will flip the ship over, toss her head over heels and break her back.

In 1992 the deepwater fishing boat *Fairwind* sank with great rapidity on Georges Bank, off Newfoundland, an area notorious for storms, fog banks and confused seas. The boat was in a rapidly developing storm with winds about 80 knots and seas of 50-plus feet when the disaster occurred. The sole survivor said the ship 'surfed down a wave, buried her bow and the following very steep 70-foot wave got under the stern and flipped the vessel end to end'.

In Wick, Scotland, a 1,350-ton breakwater was lifted and moved many yards to be dumped into the harbour; five years later a new breakwater, weighing 2,600 tons, was carried away in another storm. A half-ton boulder has been tossed 91 feet into the air at Tillmaook Rock, Oregon. A solid steel door, 195 feet above sea level, was blasted in on Unst Light in the Shetland Islands. The power of storm waves actually stopped the revolving of the light on Trinidad Head Light, 196 feet above sea level; while the pneumatic power of a wave surging *back* has sucked open the bolted iron doors of the Eddystone Lighthouse. The lighthouse on Dunnet Head, standing on the summit of a 300-foot cliff at the entrance to Pentland Firth, has had its 2-inch-thick windows repeatedly broken by stones tossed up by waves, demonstrating their abrasive power

Above A fluid and beautiful breaker so loved by surfers, showing the classic tube shape.

Overleaf In fierce storms, violent waves can assault the top of even the highest and strongest lighthouse.

and how, in conjunction with tides and currents they can affect coastlines by wearing them away or depositing sand and gravel elsewhere.

Elements of the Freak Wave

Current knowledge about freak waves comes from actual though rare and often disputed observations through the years: from sea measurements taken by special devices and trained personnel on weather ships and offshore oil rigs, from the result of a wave's onslaught on vessels and from extrapolating the meteorological records of hurricanes, typhoons and North Atlantic winter gales.

As already explained, *normal* waves are mounds of water that are raised by the transfer of energy from the wind to the sea surface. Even in large storms and hurricanes/typhoons, waves, though random, have general characteristics. They have a longer dimension across the wind/wave direction than along it. They have flattened crests with the highest part of the wave generally centred and the height falling off, both to the right and left of the wave centre. The wave centre or crest has the most potential energy and moves faster than the rest of the wave in an arc spreading or dispersing forward and to the right and left. They continue to form, surge forward and disappear. That is the normal, energy-dispersive wave.

Waves in open sea generally have a random look; that is, they vary in size and travel at different, though constant, speeds from each other and in various directions. As the components continuously get into and out of step with each other, they produce groups of high waves followed by intervals of relatively quiet water which are characteristic of all sea waves. Sometimes fast-moving wave trains will catch up with slow-moving ones heading in the same direction or waves coming at angles to one another will converge. Usually when this happens the waves are out of sync with one another – the crest of one wave will coincide with the trough of another – and they cancel each other out. The danger arises when for a brief moment two wave trains going in the same direction 'get in step' and produce a wave that is higher than either component. Infrequently, three or more wave trains get in step, concentrating their bulk, energy and motion in a single monster wave. The life of such a wave is only transient, lasting perhaps a moment or two. Because each wave component is travelling at its own characteristic speed the faster ones will escape from the others and the monster will die. The energy it contains belongs to its component wave trains which still exist and travel on, taking their energy with them.

The Extreme Storm Wave is a different thing in many ways. It behaves much like the energy-conserving swell which crosses oceans. With the level, 'horizon to horizon' crest, water is moving at the same speed all along the wave. The crest cannot disperse energy to the right or to the left and the often deadly trough ahead of the ESW apparently provides a stabilizing or balancing effect which allows the ESW to persist for long periods. Most of the descriptions of ESW mention 'foam along the crest' and 'ready to break' but few, if any, mention actual cases of breaking.

Many elements come into play in the making of an ESW. The intensity of the wind; the length of time it blows; the distance over which it blows (the fetch); prevailing

weather conditions; sea and air temperature; a series of close storms; swells arriving from storms in remote regions; sea currents; bottom topography – all these factors can affect sea state and hence monster wave formation.

Are Waves Getting Bigger?

Due to climate changes and other factors still little understood it is possible that waves are getting bigger. 'The waves are getting bigger and we don't know why. If it keeps going up, it's quite important. The energy of waves goes up with the square of the height,' says Stephen Salter, Professor of Engineering at Edinburgh University. In other words, the doubling of the height of waves could quadruple the potential damage to coastal and offshore structures.

Erik Bock, a surface chemist at the Woods Hole Oceanographic Institute in Massachusetts, says he has seen reports that Atlantic wave heights in some areas have doubled over the last decade or so and he suggests that 'the increase may be due to a decline in plankton in the Atlantic'. Apparently plankton produce a natural chemical whose calming effect on the sea is similar to that of oil on water. (In some parts of the world native divers carry oil in their mouths to release underwater to calm the waves when they dive for pearls or sponges.) Are plankton declining because of ecological disasters and environmental carelessness? According to a paper published in *Nature* by Plymouth Marine Laboratories' Chris Reid *et al*, phytoplankton is declining due to climatic changes in the North Atlantic.

Freak waves can capsize vessels of all sizes. Small boats, such as this fishing boat, are particularly vulnerable, with Lloyd's Shipping Register reporting literally thousands of unexplained disappearances each year.

Hans Graber, Professor of Applied Marine Physics at the University of Miami, who specializes in waves, also believes that the Atlantic is getting stormier, possibly due to the effects of global climate change. People who have done computer simulations on the effect of global climate change have seen the same effect in their models. One thing is certain, according to Graber: 'The Atlantic has become stormier in the past few years. At least three storms in that time have battered parts of the northeastern United States or the Canadian Maritime Provinces with waves as high as 100 feet. That clearly has ramifications for the offshore industries.'

Giant underwater waves

Waves so strong they can toss submarines about with the same kind of power their counterparts use to capsize ships on the surface also exist under the water. But while the maximum height of a freak storm surface wave seems not much over 100 feet, these mammoth undersea waves reach heights of 300 feet, and are capable of trapping shoals of fish in fjords, causing mudslides and hurling boulders from undersea mountains.

Norm Catto, Professor of Geography at Memorial University of Newfoundland and a specialist in wave analysis, has been conducting regular measurements of storm damage along the Newfoundland coast to determine heights of waves. 'Wave heights appear to have been getting higher and certainly the frequency of storms seems to be increasing,' he confirms.

Computer models suggest that as global warming increases, the North Atlantic around Greenland and Iceland will actually get colder and the severity of North Atlantic storms will increase. According to Catto, 'The general storm activity seems to have increased. They are more frequent and more violent.' But, like most scientists, he believes that in order to show any valid pattern, 1,000 years of records should be available.

Jerome Nickerson, now retired from the National Weather Service (NWS) as Marine Observations programme leader in the USA, developed a formal categorization of freak waves while rewriting the Observer's Handbook for the NWS. These were sent out to shipping companies all over the world in the hope that captains would use it during a voyage to help build up records. It's a kind of log of what the sea and weather are doing on a daily basis, and the returns are coming in, helping to build a clearer picture of the severity and frequency of freak waves. Nickerson says:

'There's no easy answer to how freak waves originate. I've estimated there are eight categories. Sometimes you have to look on the other side of the ocean for what causes the freak wave that hits you on the opposite side of the same ocean. It's not a simple process; you can't rubber stamp a freak wave – they are all different and feared by mariners across the world because they're a transitory wave. In other words, ships ride over normal waves that move up and down; then here comes this freak wave – it's actually moving; it's much higher, the crest could come down and crush the ship. There are ships that have run into freak waves and just disappeared, they went right to the bottom.'

Nickerson was serving in the US Navy in 1950 as an officer on an aircraft carrier in the Mediterranean when he experienced a freak wave, a wave which he says originated from the Mistral, an exceptionally strong wind that blows seasonally from the north down the Rhône Valley into the Gulf of Lyons. They were heading for Gibraltar at the end of a tour of duty when at about 2 pm the radar operator drew his attention to a strange flicker on his screen.

'The junior officer says to me, are we meant to have land in front of us? Hey and it's moving! I realized that what we were looking at was not the coast of Spain but a huge mass of fast-moving water.' Very soon they picked up a series of waves through their binoculars. As officer of the deck, Nickerson had responsibility for the safety of the carrier. He turned the ship bow-on to the approaching wave and blew the collision alarm. The captain arrived on the bridge just in time to see the impact. They were hit by three successive waves – a three-sisters wave – the second being the biggest at between 40 and 50 feet. Typical of a freak wave, it had that white moustache at the top which never quite seems to break.

'All of a sudden a wave comes up, moving at 30 miles an hour, about 50 feet high and it looks like it's going to eat you – what can you do? The carrier came to a dead stop in the water, it was just like hitting a brick wall. We wiped out all the china in the ward room.'

The fact that it was daylight, that there had been time to sound the alarm and that there were no aircraft on deck, saved the ship from serious damage and loss of life. Nevertheless, the experience was not one Nickerson wished to repeat. 'I was really scared, frightened to death. I didn't think these things existed at the time,' he says.

A similar wave was experienced by another US aircraft carrier, the *Independence*, in April 1977. The captain recalls: 'It was raining. I looked out ahead, I'd estimate a mile to a mile and a half and I saw what appeared to me to be a significant wave coming. This thing was just like *The Poseidon Adventure*.' Four 60-foot waves jarred into the *Independence* during that storm, fortunately causing little damage.

Jerome Nickerson also experienced a bizarre ESW that came out of nowhere and surged up on shore at Daytona Beach during the preparations for the Independence Day celebrations on 3 July 1992. 'There were many cars on the beach when the 20-foot wave hit. Evidently it had broken several times at sea and was now only white water. However, it still had a lot of force as it hit shore and there were cars bobbing around like bath toys.'

Can Freak Waves be Predicted?

It is a well-known saying that you can't tame the sea any more than you can catch the wind. The sea in all its many moods is the breeding ground for random monster waves. A single area of stormy ocean can produce any number of giant waves. Wave trains will, just by chance, coincide and produce a large wave which will have its brief moment of glory, a transient, awesome heap of water well over 100 feet high that charges through the sea, eventually breaking in a kind of horizontal avalanche – perhaps to overwhelm a ship or perhaps to be seen by no one – before the components separate and the wave disappears for ever into the random jumble of the sea. Elsewhere in the storm the same conditions exist for other monster waves to form. The

Opposite above Men struggle to clean up after the disastrous oil spill when the *Exxon Valdez* was wrecked in fierce storms off Alaska.

Opposite below In 1967 when the *Torrey Canyon* broke up off the Scilly Isles, it was brutally brought home to the government that they didn't know how to deal with the resulting oil spill: in the end, they sent bombers to blow up the wreck and burn off the oil.

Below A sea bird struggles for its life in the *Exxon Valdez* oil spill.

laws of probability say that this is certain to occur, but they say nothing about where or when. Even present-day computers are unable to handle it. In most cases, there is no way as yet of warning ships when and where the giants will strike.

There are a few exceptions: certain places or situations where the probability of dangerous waves is far higher than normal and where they can, in principle, be avoided. Such predictable exceptions are where there are obstacles such as islands or breakwaters that force waves to change their direction or shape; and where conflicting wind/tide/ocean currents occur, such as the powerful Agulhas Current which flows off the so-called 'Wild Coast' of South Africa, usually in conflict with the prevailing winds (see page 24). Waves split when they approach an island then bend and wrap themselves around it. When the divided waves converge on the far (lee) side they can reach unexpectedly large heights, casting doubt on the traditional recommendation to ships of finding shelter behind an island during a storm.

Waves and Ecological Disasters

The public is becoming more aware of the dangers of freak waves. Although several other ships came through unscathed, in 1966 the 44,000-ton *Michaelangelo* took a terrific beating inside and out in a fierce April storm some 800 miles from New York, off Newfoundland, where savage seas exist for several months each year. With 775 passengers, she was suddenly struck by an enormous wave which inundated the entire forward half of the ship, breaking heavy glass 80 feet above the waterline. A large hole was gouged in the ship's curved superstructure. Forty feet of railing and bulwark were torn away. Seventy feet above the sea, tons of water crushed bulkheads and cascaded into the ship.

Two passengers and a crewman died, many were injured. Passengers spoke of terror as the vast length of the liner 'seemed to whip back and forth as though she were flexible'. The *Michaelangelo* limped into port and thousands of New Yorkers gazed in awe at the twisted metal high above the waterline, asking could this really be the work of a single wave?

The answer is yes. Thousands of seagoing craft around the world – liners, tankers, trawlers, warships, pleasurecraft – as well as assorted offshore structures, have had similar meetings with that most dangerous of maritime phenomena. And if a single wave can inflict that kind of damage on the *Michaelangelo* for everyone to see, or sink a 100,000-ton tanker with all modern navigational aids, then obviously the contents of vessels sent to sea, the sealanes used, and the role of offshore structures must be carefully examined if worse disasters are not to occur.

Research into waves is now a billion-dollar business as oil companies seek to ensure that their oil platforms are safe and that their super-tankers, with thousands of gallons of crude oil, do not break up and spill oil into the sea, causing the kind of ecological damage that gains them outraged universal condemnation as in the case of the *Exxon Valdez*. Offshore oil rigs are now designed for the maximum wave that it is anticipated could occur within any one area in the 30-year or so life of the rigs; but tankers still sail a dangerous path.

Today the sea is the main road for the transport of oil and huge tankers carry hundreds of thousands of barrels across the great oceans. It should be possible to choose safer routes or, even, to proscribe certain routes or simply not to send tankers to sea in certain months where it is highly probable that storms might wreck them. They hit reefs, burst open and lose their oil in rough seas. Our need for fuel is fouling the coastline and killing wildlife. It might even be killing off the very plankton that helps calm the sea. The first sign of any trouble was the 1967 wreck of the tanker *Torrey Canyon*. In lashing winter seas, the tanker hit a reef off the British Isles and broke open. The oil seeped out and covered shores for miles. Sea birds and animals died by the thousands. Toxic detergents which were meant to break up the oil killed more marine life. Eventually the British government dispatched RAF bombers which destroyed and burned the tanker and the remaining oil.

This was the beginning. Since then scores of accidents have oiled the sea and killed our wildlife, even in the most pristine parts of the ocean. We may need oil to lubricate our civilization, but we shouldn't forget that to reach us it may encounter freak waves, oceanic giants that we cannot control or always predict.

Tsunami

One of the most poignant sentences uttered after the tsunami that devastated Papua New Guinea's remote northern coastline in 1998 came from Dickson Dalle, the district rescue co-ordinator, who said: 'There is little point in

Papua New Guinea: devastation after two undersea earthquakes caused a tsunami which killed over 2,000 people.

rebuilding the schools because we don't have the children. They're all dead.'

A string of seven villages, built of jungle materials on a narrow spit of land sandwiched between the sea and a lagoon, were utterly destroyed on the night of 17 July after an earthquake 12 miles inland, with an epicentre 20 miles below the surface and measuring 7.0 on the Richter scale, heralded a disaster about to happen. Fourteen minutes later another earthquake, of magnitude 5.7, 12 miles out to sea, sent a 30-foot wall of water racing ashore. It was all over within twenty minutes. More than 2,000 people were killed, washed out of their homes into the lagoon beyond or sucked out to sea in the powerful backsurge as the waters withdrew.

Survivors reported that the wave sounded 'like a jet engine' roaring towards them. 'We just saw the sea rise up and it came towards the village and we had to run for our lives,' said Paul Saroya, who lost eight members of his family.

Eddie Michael had just begun preparing an evening meal for her family when she felt the earthquake. The approaching wave 'sounded like warplanes were coming. When we looked out to the sea we could see this big wave coming, and it was like a big mountain,' she said.

Lusien Romme felt three shakes from the offshore earthquake, then saw 'the sea rising up and coming towards me'. In terror, he fled for his life away from the wave, which he said was as tall as the coconut trees around his home. In the space of just two minutes, he was shouting to his wife and the villagers to save themselves, desperately searching for his six-year-old daughter Martina, who was out playing with friends, before the wave crashed into his flimsy hut and swept it away – along with the entire village. The wave hurled him high into a coconut tree and then carried him into the lagoon, where he surfaced in darkness with hundreds of drowned bodies all around him. 'I cried for help. I called for anyone who was alive. I was really scared,' he said. Later, he found his daughter, who was safe; but his wife had drowned.

So many had died that Apuan, a fisherman, was unable to count the bodies in the water, as two days later he paddled his canoe through the surf to the sea. 'In one place, there were so many bodies together I had to move the boat slowly to pass through them,' he said. Because entire families were wiped out and dogs were feeding on the corpses, there was no time to treat the dead with any ceremony. The lagoon was so packed with bodies rapidly decomposing in the equatorial heat that it was decided to fill it in, while the bodies on land were covered with palm mats and burned with kerosene.

The Historical Picture

Reports of the Papua New Guinea tsunami were flashed round the world, complete with satellite-beamed photographs, within hours of its happening; but since ancient times there have been stories of the great waves that suddenly rise from nowhere out of the sea and devastate coastal settlements. One of the earliest tsunamis on record took place on the eastern shores of the Mediterranean in AD 358. It passed completely over islands and low-lying shores, leaving boats on the housetops of Alexandria and drowning thousands of people.

Was Noah's flood the first recorded example of a tsunami? Scientists now theorize that a massive tsunami backed by floods lasting 150 days could have led to this Bible story.

There's even a theory that Noah's flood could have been the first recorded tsunami. Scientists investigating a large tsunami originating in the Arabian Sea in 1945 speculated that the biblical story could well have been based on a massive tsunami that inundated the Tigris and Euphrates rivers for 150 days 5,000 years ago.

The Making of a Tsunami

Imagine dropping a rock in the centre of a calm pond and watching the ripples spread outwards to lap against the banks. That is how the waves behave in a tsunami – only the cause is not a rock being dropped but an earthquake about 20 or 30 miles beneath an ocean floor sending seismic shock waves upwards and outwards throughout the Earth's crust and the ocean from the point of the earthquake's epicentre. The waves are not just on the surface layer, as in the confused patterns of wind-generated waves described earlier, but they are in straight lines, many miles long, that travel both vertically from the bottom to the top of even the deepest ocean, while moving along horizontally at great speed – something like a chorus-line of gigantic seahorses in motion with barely the tips of their ears showing. The maximum height of an underwater tsunami could be 16,400 feet, although this has never been measured. But if one that size were to travel through the depths of the abyss it would make barely a ripple on the surface and would pass under ships without anyone realizing it was there. Frequently these waves are strong enough to cross entire oceans and will devastate all islands and coastal regions in their path. They can reach speeds of up to 500 miles an hour.

As tsunamis approach land a number of changes take place. As the sea floor shelves up to the coast, waves begin to 'feel bottom'. The resulting friction gradually slows down their forward momentum, causing a rising up as the wavelength (that is, the distance between two crests) is shortened. This is what, in principle, happens with normal waves – but they collapse and break when their height becomes more than seven times the length between two crests, while in a tsunami the amount of power is stupendous. Thousands of feet of vertical power is compressed as the waves reach shore. The waves are in effect pushed closer together while the massive sum of their displaced kinetic energy is transferred upward into fearsome vertical monsters that have nowhere to go but on land.

A tsunami is rarely a single monster wave but rather a series of successive surges spaced fifteen minutes to an hour or more apart. The *American Practical Navigator* reports that the most damage is inflicted between the third and eighth waves. This is preceded by a sure sign of doom: withdrawal of sea which occurs when a tsunamic trough reaches land, causing massive outflow of water far beyond lowest ebb tide. As water recedes, people hear a terrible cacophony of hissing, rattling and boiling as pebbles, rocks and shells are drawn out to sea. Whole bays have been emptied in minutes, stranding marine animals and exposing marine wrecks to view. In the past people rushed out to examine these unexpected discoveries. Moments later, with a tragic sense of irony and timing, the sea returned with the sound of an express train to drown the curious.

After an earthquake in Japan in 1793, people on the coast of Tugaru were so terrified by the extraordinary ebbing of the sea they scurried to higher ground. When a second quake came, they dashed back to the beach, fearing that they might be buried under landslides. Just as they reached the shore, the first huge tsunami wave crashed down upon them, killing them all.

In 1868 a stretch of nearly 300 miles of the west coast of America was shaken by earthquakes. Shortly after the most violent shocks the sea receded from the shore, leaving ships that had been anchored in 40 feet of water stranded in mud – then a greater wave returned and boats were carried a quarter of a mile inland.

Sometimes, when an underwater earthquake close to land results in a deep rift or chasm in the sea bed, another kind of trough, or backsurge, can occur when the sea literally falls into the bowels of the earth, like water going down the plug-hole. Everything from deep-sea creatures to, theoretically, submarines could vanish into this pit, creating a giant abyssal whirlpool which draws billions upon billions of tons of water to it until the rift is filled, or closes. At the same time, seismic shock waves have formed the classic tsunami which ripples ever outwards towards land.

Tsunamis can move at incredible speeds and build to awesome heights. Their forward speed is in direct proportion to the depth of water through which they pass. The deeper the water, the faster they race along the surface, travelling at 650 miles an hour over waters with a 30,000-feet depth and at 115 miles an hour over a 900-foot depth. Spreading out like the ripples on a pond, they can journey halfway around the world, some rebounding onto land and bouncing back and forth across the sea for a week or more. The waves can grow up to 220 feet in height and have probably killed millions over the ages. The force they exert is incredible. Even a relatively modest tsunami 30 feet high, travelling at 45 miles an hour, exerts 49 tons of pressure per square yard.

The shape of the coastline influences the height and strength of a tsunami. Deep water close to shore limits damage, as can offshore reefs, which reduce their power; while in places where there is shelving coastline, incoming tsunamis have time to build up to devastating heights. The most fatal places are where there is a V-shaped inlet or harbour; here, a tsunami acts like a river bore, its power and height accelerating as it is rapidly compressed on all sides.

Volcanoes That Make Tsunamis

Underwater volcanic explosions can also cause tsunamis. The greatest explosion of historic times was the small island of Krakatoa, in the Sunda Strait between Java and Sumatra. On 26 August 1883, Krakatoa was obliterated by 95-foot waves after a volcanic eruption that also disturbed the sea bed. More than 36,000 people were killed in the surrounding region.

Krakatoa literally exploded, the sudden inrush of sea water adding to the fury of superheated steam in the cauldron. When the inferno of white-hot lava, molten rock, steam and smoke finally subsided, the island that had stood 1,400 feet above the sea had become a cavity 1,000 feet below sea level. Only along one edge of the former crater did a remnant of the island remain.

The tsunami wave – by now more than 100 feet high – wiped out villages along the Strait and killed tens of thousands of people; it was felt on the shores of the Indian Ocean and onwards to Cape Horn. Rounding the Cape into the Atlantic it sped northwards as far as the English Channel. The sound of the explosion was heard in the Philippine Islands, in Australia, and on the island of Madagascar nearly 3,000 miles away. And the pulverized heart of Krakatoa ascended into the stratosphere, to be carried around the globe as dust-clouds, producing spectacular sunsets in every country of the world for almost a year.

Ring of Fire

Most tsunamis are born on the deepest trenches of the ocean floor. The Japanese, Aleutian and Atacama trenches, all on the Pacific 'Ring of Fire' zone, have each produced gigantic waves that have claimed many human lives. On the day in 1998 that the tsunami devastated Papua New Guinea's northern shoreline, three other earthquakes of half the magnitude had occurred in a broad sweep from Sumatra to Fiji, causing little or no damage. Such abyssal trenches are, by their very nature, breeders of earthquakes, places of buckling and warping downward of the sea floor, to form the deepest chasms of the Earth's surface, where the crust is already relatively thin.

In Japan, possibly the nation most prone to earthquakes, lying as it does on a seismically active region, the threat of tsunamis is not only from earthquakes generated half a world away, but from those quite close to home. Many Japanese

This dramatic poster from the classic movie *Krakatoa – East of Java* has all the elements of what actually happened when the volcano blew on 26 August 1883, causing death and destruction as massive tsunami waves surged over neighbouring coastal lands.

depend on the sea to earn a living; but they also know that its bounty can be matched by its wrath. Regularly, they have festivals and make offerings to the gods of the sea – with little result, it seems.

On 26 June 1896, all Japan gathered to celebrate *Sanno-sai* – 'Boys' Festival'. Three hundred miles north of Tokyo, at the fishing town of Sanriku, the revelry was at its height, with dragon banners waving, coloured lanterns flickering, the beat of drums and the chime of bells – when an earthquake 120 miles offshore jolted the 32,000-foot floor of the Tuscarora Deep. Billions of gallons of sea water were sucked deep into a gaping gash in the Earth's crust. Within twenty minutes, the sea started to recede from the shore, silencing the familiar roar of the surf; but, happy in their noisy revelry, nobody in Sanriku noticed.

A whisper came, then a hiss, then a roar as a 110-foot wave raced back across the naked sea bed.

Horror-stricken, the revellers tried to run, but doom literally fell on their heads. Millions of tons of water engulfed the coast for hundreds of miles. Entire villages and 27,122 lives were lost. And yet, 20 miles offshore, the fishermen of Sanriku, who had forgone the festival to work that night, had no idea of the disaster that had befallen their families and friends. On returning to shore the next morning, they found nothing remained, just corpses floating in the surf and the wreckage of their homes.

Other Kinds of Tsunami

Most tsunamis are created by undersea earthquakes or volcanoes but similar effects are created in other ways: submarine avalanches (Block Island off Rhode Island); glaciers or landslides falling into the sea (Lituya Bay, Alaska); massive explosions in the sea, including, so it is warned, nuclear blasts (although there is no real evidence to prove this claim) – and even falling meteorites, which is what many scientists believe happened when a meteorite more than 6 miles across, with ten billion times the energy of an atomic bomb, fell partly into the sea and partly on land on Mexico's Yucatan Peninsula some 65 million years ago. (Many people think that this meteorite triggered the mass extinction that wiped out the dinosaurs.)

Undersea Landslides

Some sports fishermen off Baja, California, suddenly heard a sound similar to a boat running aground on a rocky reef, although they were

Main picture Dangerous yet beautiful: 'The Great Wave of Kanagawa', by Japanese artist Hukusai Katsushika (1760–1849) is the classic image that so eloquently sums up the incredible height and force of a tsunami. These killer waves devastate earthquake-prone Japan more than any other region of the world.

Inset A submarine earthquake off the coast of Japan sends a 100-foot tsunami surging inland, causing widespread panic and disaster as people and cars are washed away and buildings are destroyed.

over a sandy bottom with plenty of calm water under the keel. Glancing around, they saw astern to the north a single wave approaching fast out of nowhere.

If caught in the shallows they knew their boat could be dashed on to rocks and coral so they raced westward out to sea to meet the wave in deeper water as it continued to rise. Finally, they turned their boat into the wave and met it bow-on at nearly maximum speed. The bow continued to rise until it was tilted upward at about 45 to 50 degrees. Suddenly the bow broke through the wave and the boat was airborne. After a short flight it crashlanded with no apparent damage. As quickly as it had come, the freak wave had gone and the sea was glassy calm again, leaving the fishermen baffled. Enquiries informed them that possibly this unexpected wave was caused by an underwater landslide, one of several that frequently occur on the rocky California coast.

Underwater landslides just offshore can cause moderate, though still unwelcome, damage to those at sea.

A school outing off Rhode Island almost ended in disaster when a deep 'trench' opened up in the sea in front of their boat. The school party was on the *Super Squirrel*, a 110-foot aluminium-hulled converted sub chaser, heading south to watch whales a few miles southeast of Block Island when someone spotted what appeared to be the double wave of another vessel near the island. It was a clear day with little wind and wave activity and there were no other ships around that could have caused the waves. But there was something odd about these waves, which were in a long straight line moving rapidly towards them.

As the line got closer the captain could see two parallel waves about 3–4 feet high with a darker area, about 20–30 yards wide, between them. 'I turned slowly to meet it bow-on as a precaution – when to my horror, I saw that this dark area was a huge trench several miles long.'

Another observer estimated the trough to be at least 40 feet deep. The bow of the *Super Squirrel* pitched up slightly over the lead wave and then fell to 'at least 50 or 60 degrees down angle' before being buried in the icy sea. It came up rapidly so they took on little water. One of the passengers was washed overboard and was rescued quickly; several others suffered broken bones and bruises. In the confusion, no one noticed where the freak waves went after they passed. Later, scuba divers found evidence of an underwater landslide near Block Island that had caused this 'mini-tsunami' surge.

The Good Friday Tsunami

Tsunamis can affect regions which have never heard of them. On Good Friday, 27 March 1964, a violent earthquake off the coast of Alaska generated an enormous tsunami. The entire Pacific coast of mainland USA, from Vancouver to Denver, lay in its path. At eleven o'clock that night in Oregon, Crescent City's civil defence chief, Bill Parker, received a teletype warning him about the tsunami, giving him the estimated time of arrival. He didn't even know what a tsunami was, let alone spell it. But once they'd checked into what to expect and the news got out, many citizens were curious and flocked to the waterfront to watch the waves come in, simply not realizing the danger. When the wave arrived – and kept on coming in – people started to run. For some it was too late. Carnival atmosphere gave way to sheer panic and terror as the entire town was inundated.

Dumbfounded, Bill Parker telephoned the governor: 'I think Crescent City's gone,' he said.

Since then, the town has rebuilt itself and, although they have no sea wall or computerized warning system in place, the people regularly have tsunami practice. The children of Oregon are familiar with a flood legend which possibly described a previous seismic wave. Local Native American tribes tell a story in which a grandmother warned two children to run as fast as they could away from the harbour. Halfway up the hill, they looked back. They could see the water come in and they could hear people crying. When the sun came up in the morning, everything was gone.

In that long-ago example, it's more than likely that the tsunami did not originate in Alaska but right on the doorstep. Just offshore of Crescent City and several thousand feet down, lies the Cascadia subduction zone, a 900-mile crack in the Earth's crust. A geological slip here – and a tsunami would engulf the coast in twenty minutes. Because of the risk, Oregon has established a 300-mile-long inundation zone, where no new schools or hospitals can be built close to shore. But it is a terrifying thought that a great tragedy is waiting to happen: in the summer months forty to fifty thousand people are often out on the shore at any one time at the local resort area of Longbeach – too far out to get to safety in time should there be an earthquake on the Cascadia rift.

Tsunamis in many sizes and shapes can affect any part of Earth. They can affect our lives when we least expect them. Warnings help; good seamanship can help. But, ultimately, a tsunami is one thing we can do little to escape. If confronted with one, it really is a matter of life – or death.

The Surfer's Wave

Windsurfers and boardsurfers are gamblers, and what they gamble is not money, or possessions – but their lives. For decades, they have searched the world for the ultimate wave, travelling from Hawaii to Tiree in the Outer Hebrides, from Australia to Florida. They will try the Atlantic coast of France and the Pacific coast of California; they will brave sharks off the Wild Coast of South Africa and Matanchen Bay, Mexico. They get a high from pitting their wits and their strength against some of the most dangerous waves possible; and those who die, far from being called fools, are covered in glory and talked of with awe by the aficionados. They are the kind of people who make – and buy – a video called *Total Insanity* because, to most people, what real surf bums do for fun is totally insane.

The ultimate wave is the most dynamic and exciting thing in the world to surfers, who will remember it in their dreams for ever if the meeting of sea and mind and body has been significant – the ride of their lives. There are surfers who enjoy a battle with the elements who will only go out in a force-8 gale, or will even try to surf off the coast of Florida during a hurricane. For windsurfers, and indeed boardsurfers, 'Jaws' is arguably the most awesome, the mightiest, the most dangerous wave in the world. It is a 300-foot-long wave break at the edge of an outer reef about a mile off the northeast shore of the island of Maui, in Hawaii. At its most ferocious, it's capable of producing 50–60-foot waves that barrel over with astonishing force, hurling huge quantities of white water onto a jagged reef. Wave-sailor Chris Calthrop, who became the first Briton to surf Jaws, in February 1997, describes it:

> '*This sonic boom of a bang went off as the wave collapsed 10 feet behind me. It sounded and felt like a bus had just been dropped out of the sky on its side and landed right behind me. In fact, the volume of water was probably ten times as heavy as any bus. That would seriously just slam you into pieces. At that instant I threw a glance back... and up. Way above me was towering this totally, utterly, awesome wall of water. It must have been four storeys high – just huge – and still barrelling heavily. The mouth of the barrel alone was 20 feet in diameter. For a split second I stared right into that gaping mouth. Unbelievable. Such an amazing place. Such a dangerous place. And the realization hit me instantly. What a perfect name. Jaws! Enter at your peril!*'

An elite band of surfers and wave-sailors are mesmerized by this ocean phenomenon and refer to it as a 'living entity'. Jaws occurs only a few times each year, usually between November and March, and depends on specific meteorological conditions; basically a huge northerly swell rolling 2–3,000 miles across the Pacific, generated by a big storm in the Aleutian Islands, which in turn comes from low pressures going around the North Pole. The first shallow spot that the swell hits after its long, uninterrupted southerly ocean journey is an outer reef off Maui which cuts into the bottom of the wave, causing it to jack up and pitch forward into the classic massive tube or pipe. With no gradual land shelf to slow it down, Jaws powers in from deep water incredibly fast, 25–30 miles an hour. This phenomenon can have a disconcerting effect – a surfer can appear to be travelling backwards up the wave if he is not going fast enough. If Jaws wipes you out you are in serious trouble.

Plunging breakers are the most dynamic and exciting manifestations of wave action; their rounded backs and concave fronts occur where they suddenly hit land – or, in the case of Hawaii, a reef. There is a sudden deficiency of water ahead of the wave which is moving at open-water speed. Water in the trough rushes seaward with great force to fill the cavity in the incoming wave. With insufficient water to complete the classic rounded wave form, the water in the crest, attempting to complete its natural orbit, is hurled ahead of its steep forward slide and falls back in on itself, making the long, shoreward rolling and dangerous pipe so beloved of surfers.

Schoolteacher Fred Van Dyke has never forgotten the late evening in the early 1950s when he was at a surfing area known as Big Steamer Lane, off Santa Cruz, California, an evening which perhaps explains the lure of surfing: 'A sea lion pops out of the wave and starts surfing, throwing water off its chest... all of a sudden ahead of me, a 45-pound salmon jumps completely out of the water, and it's shimmering in the last bits of golden sunlight, but it's also shimmering on the other side from the moonlight...'

But it's not all magical beauty. This is what happened to boardsurfer John Severson when he did battle with the notorious Makaha Bowl on Hawaii.

'We raced across the longest big wave I'd ever ridden. I looked back and saw a great tube with a pouring lip that looked six feet thick where it impacted on the flat water... we paddled back over a few waves, then an incredibly large green beauty looked at an almost perfect peak... the wave was jumping fast, and as I started down I back-pedalled into position and raced down the face of a bona fide big wave. I hadn't looked around during the last moments of paddling and was now shocked to see that the peak had rippled ahead and I was turning into an incredible wall with a section fifty yards ahead already leaping out into space. This was the famous – and dangerous – Makaha Bowl... I thought if I straighten out I'm going to get nailed by the tube, so my only chance is to use my speed and do a pointed dive into the wall and try to get beneath and maybe through the back.

I speared deep into the wave and everything went quiet. I'd made it. I remember no rush of water. Only hitting the bottom feet first, like I'd just jumped out of a second-storey window. I'd been swept over the falls in the lip; which then drilled through some 30 feet of water with me caught in the moving lip, and so I felt almost no water resistance. And there I was, squashed into a squatting position on the ocean floor, but still quite alive...

After a few seconds I decided to push off and test the going. I was shocked to find I couldn't move – not even unbend from the squatting

Above Windsurfers battling with exhilarating surf-capped rollers off Tiree in the Outer Hebrides.

Below A windsurfer flies over foam-capped rollers off Diamond Head, Hawaii.

position... I held as long as I could... then pushed off and started up, but was slammed back to the bottom.

Things were getting critical... I was blacking out... I came back to consciousness and pushed off again. It was still churning but I wasn't losing ground. Euphoria swept me. My life flashed by... and the realization that I was paying for high adventure with my life.'

Main picture and inset
Champion windsurfer Robby Seeger and friends ride 'Jaws', off Maui in Hawaii – one of the most dangerous surfers' waves in the world, conquered by only a handful of daredevils.

Severson made it to the surface in the trough of the next wave and lived to tell the tale. Unlike most surfers, this mighty wave did not give him a taste for bigger and better; he still surfed, but settled for smaller.

When Jaws is sailable or surfable it's never small. It's extremely difficult and dangerous to swim or sail out to this famous wave because of the sheer cliffs that face out towards the reef. And after, there is no graceful ride into a sloping beach on Jaws itself because the sea breaks right on the base of the cliff. Even if you manage to overcome that, there is the danger of sharks. In fact, for a long time, Jaws was thought to be an impossible wave to ride, so terrifying that no one tried it until the early 1990s. Since that first attempt, there have been several near-fatalities.

According to Chris Calthrop: 'As the wave lands, you can feel the power. There's a shock of thousands of tons of weight going through the water. It explodes with an awesome sound. This wave could probably rip your limbs off. Then at the bottom of the cliffs, huge boulders are rolling around on the bottom. You can hear the rumble from two miles away – in fact, people who live on the cliffs can't sleep at night when there's a storm, for the sound of the boulders. You have to land in just the right place, and have a jet-ski or boat right there to pull you out.'

Long before man used flat boards for surfing on waves, sea creatures such as porpoises and penguins were using the energy of waves to travel through the sea by sliding down the forward surface of an advancing wave. It is not known how long ago Polynesians used to surf with their boats on giant waves – nor how long ago they brought this ancient sport with them to Hawaii, although Captain Cook had seen Hawaiians surfing on canoes in 1771. However, it was first recorded by a British naval officer, Lieutenant James King, in Hawaii eight years later, in 1779.

Off Maui, Hawaii: windsurfer Robby Seeger at the base of a 30-foot tube about to form above his head.

Hollow surfboards were invented in 1929 and plastic foam boards in 1956. The newest variation on the natural energy-saving device developed by sea creatures is the sport of surfboard sailing or wind surfing. Invented by Hoyle Schweitzer in California in 1967, wind surfing has become popular across the world. The wind surfer looks like a conventional surfboard but is twice as long and considerably thicker. On top of the board is a single sail that the rider controls from a standing position while gliding along. Wind surfers can be launched in thirty seconds, but the sport is harder than it looks, requiring good balance. A wall of air is trapped in the sail and the body weight has to balance against the pull of the wind. Three important skills to master are: putting the sail on a 90-degree angle to the wind (beam reach); coming about; and bringing the wind surfer back to the shore. It is a safe sport because the sail automatically falls when the rider lets go – which is often immediately.

According to most surfers and sailboarders, Hawaii overall has the best waves in the world. Low pressure systems spin off the bottom of Alaska or Japan, generating waves with a very long fetch over a very long period. These waves travel fast and freely over thousands of miles – possibly the fastest of ocean waves outside tsunamis and freak waves – pushed along by intense pressure systems, in a broad sweep from Hawaii to California. High pressure systems create the northeast trade winds that sweep Hawaii and these two factors together go to make the perfect surfing wave.

Some surfing superlatives

Highest consistent surfing wave
The 30–35-foot monsters at Makaha Beach, Hawaii.

Longest ride possible on a surfboard
Probably a distance of 5,700 feet on great waves that break four to six times a year in Matanchen Bay near Santa Blas, Nayarit, Mexico.

Longest recorded ride
Almost one mile, which surfing champion Tom Blake took off Waikiki Beach in June 1936. Blake rode to the shore on a 25-foot-high wall of water stretching across the full length of Waikiki Bay, something that rarely happens. None of his companions made it to shore. (The average ride is usually just 200 yards in that location.)

Hawaii does not have a continental shelf; the islands are the tops of ancient volcanoes sitting in the middle of the Pacific. The full strength of the unrestricted power of the waves fetching up here comes from deep water suddenly hitting offshore coral reefs, with no gently shelving undersea slopes to slow them down. In fact, coral grows as close as possible to the surface under the sea in order to get sunlight; so off Hawaii is a situation where massive, fast-moving mounds of water suddenly come up against an obstruction.

Surfers read and watch and check every weather forecast available of swells and winds to try and gauge if it's going to be a good surf day. Chris Calthrop, originally from the Kent coast of England, bases himself for much of the year on the island of Maui in Hawaii. He climbs up a tree and from there has a panoramic view of a huge horseshoe of ocean. He uses his own instinct as a gauge; if the waves are up, in the right direction and the wind is up, then sailing Jaws is a possibility. He also checks the North Western buoy of the Hawaiian Islands report on the Internet, which more or less gives an indication of what the swell is doing at that hour. The right ingredients are a minimum of 12-foot west-by-northwest waves with a period of 17 seconds – that is, crests 17 seconds apart.

The Day Chris Calthrop Rode Jaws

It was a very dramatic day. Chris had been working up to it for a while, sailing a lot of big waves further down the coast, in safer places. For a year he had been coming to study Jaws on the days it worked to get an intimate knowledge and feel of the way it ran, judging his own confidence and ability. Then one day, Chris felt ready, but he couldn't get anyone to give him a ride out. Jaws is one of the most inaccessible waves, about five miles from any beach, and you have to get there by boat or jet-ski. The tiny, elite group who had ridden this dangerous monster deemed Chris too inexperienced yet to try. Men like Robby Naish (American) and Robby Seeger (German) were some of the first to attempt and succeed in sailing Jaws and also surfboarding it when there was little or no wind. They knew the dangers – and none of them wanted to be indirectly responsible for Chris's death.

Another consideration Chris felt was that if he did swim out to Jaws from an unexpected direction, no one would know he was there making his attempt. It wasn't just that he wanted witnesses – he also wanted to be rescued if things went horribly wrong.

He drove up the cliff above Jaws and waited for two hours until he saw Naish and Seeger come out in a boat. They set up their equipment and dropped on to a couple of big waves. Chris had decided that he would take his board 3 miles downshore in order to paddle out to sea through the Maliko Gulch estuary, a murky, turbulent spot notorious for the presence of vicious tiger sharks, in order to reach Jaws from the back door. He drove down to Maliko Gulch, ignoring warnings from local people. Only two weeks before someone on a jet-ski had been attacked by tiger sharks at this very spot. Chris says:

> 'It's a bad place to be, the only place that I could conceivably get out through the surf, which was breaking heavily on the sides. But there was a gap you could swim through because there's no wind on the inside, so I decided to take the risk and swim, just take my chances with the sharks. What made it doubly dangerous was I had to sail three miles below cliffs with huge surf pounding on them. Suddenly, the fear of a shark coming up from the depths overwhelmed me and I had to jump on the board and start paddling. When I got to clearer water, I put my head in the water and had a look around... and that quelled the panic that was rising up in me.
>
> 'Then I had to sort of steer between the two headlands, which are quite close together... with pounding surf on either side. That was incredibly tense and very scary. I was in two fears – one of the surf and the other of drifting on to the rocks. It was basically the frying pan or the fire situation.'

Even though there was a boat where Chris made contact when he arrived off Jaws, Robby Naish told him that it wasn't safe without a jet-ski backup, both to tow the board into the wave and also to stand by to pick him up afterwards. Two other people had recently been eaten by the wave, and it was only the presence of a jet-ski which saved them from losing their lives. But wind surfing is Chris's passion. It was the ultimate challenge to ride the biggest wave and feel he had done it without any help.

'Calthrop's tree': from this striking lookout tree on Maui, Hawaii, British champion wave-sailor Chris Calthrop surveys the conditions across the bay to check whether surf's up.

> 'You want zero mistakes and that's the bottom line. One mistake and you're very possibly dead. Even if you survive the first wave, there are consecutive waves. The other side of it, is it's just incredible fun. Every wave is your own; it's virgin snow. There's all the fear and anticipation of actually catching a wave, but once you've caught it it's that feeling of running on water and flying at the same time multiplied ten times over...

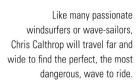

Like many passionate windsurfers or wave-sailors, Chris Calthrop will travel far and wide to find the perfect, the most dangerous, wave to ride.

twenty times the speed, the freedom, the power under your feet. There's nothing else like it.

'I first caught a couple of smaller 20-foot ones, just on the shoulder to get the feel for it; then I waited maybe 15 minutes. I was shaking, kind of nervous and said to myself, okay – this is the wave to catch – and dropped in on one that was big… maybe 40 feet. There's no turning back, you can't pull out, you can't stop it. I was travelling at full speed just to stay with the wave, and finally it started to hit the reef. At that point it slows a fraction and you can get in. I started dropping in and the wave started sucking up and I was getting elevated higher and higher and higher – I couldn't believe how high I felt. I was looking down and thinking I've got to get down there without making a mistake. There's chop, wind gusts, and all sorts of factors; and that wave was just so much speed. I was dropping in on this wave and finally got to where it was sucking smooth and I started carving out towards the channel where the waves aren't breaking and this was the first impression of power.

'Instantly, there's the shock of sound, like a sonic boom just landed behind me with a crack. I could feel the shock through my feet in the board and it scared me.

'When I finished, I looked back at the wave and was thinking, do I want to do this again? It crosses your mind, where do you stop? You know you're risking your life, but you can't be put off by other people's accidents. Jaws is the boss, Mother Nature is in control and we just play with her until finally one day she might just say, right that's enough – your day has come.

'And then this big set came in, started peaking about another 100 yards further out than all the other waves. I knew it was going to be a monster wave. I got on it and was coming in, past the point of no return. You can't pull out, you've got to go with it. It was a beautiful smooth wave. God knows what speed I was doing, an amazing speed. I was just in heaven, carving towards the shoulder and just as I started coming back up, I had time to try and look up… it's hard to describe, but basically, it's a tower block. All I could see was a suicidally huge wall of water, just a wall of water in the air. It was one of the most amazing waves I've ever ridden. It's almost like a tidal wave, it's just phenomenal and dangerous… dangerous.'

chapter two

the weather machine

Ice crystals deep under the waves that hold more reserves of fuel than all the gas, oil and coal fields combined – the releasing of which could unleash catastrophic waves and weather; massive hurricane systems born of sea and sky off the coast of Africa that take lives and cause billions of dollars' worth of damage in America; capricious winds that change direction in the Indian Ocean to bring monsoon-driven waves that can kill hundreds of thousands of people; a 'Christmas child' that wreaks havoc around the world with flood, famine and fire; terrifying typhoons with double eyes and record winds of 236 miles an hour; cyclones that rage from Newfoundland to Florida, dumping feet of snow, washing away homes and sinking ships: the weather machine that is the sea and sky combined is a fearsome monster of mythological proportions and power.

Vast fields of gas crystals have recently been found on a worldwide scale covering millions of square kilometres below the surface of the sea bed. If exploited as fuel this would dwarf all the world's reserves of coal, oil and natural gas. The crystals are formed from natural gas at low temperatures and high pressure. This gas was given off by marine bacteria over millions of years and trapped in ice-crystal structures a few metres below the ocean bed on the margins of the continental shelf.

As we move into a new millennium, scientists from thirty countries are working together through the Ocean Drilling Programme on a £60 million survey to investigate the potential of the gas crystals to meet all the world's fuel needs for the next few centuries – and beyond.

Dr Ben Clennell of the University of Leeds School of Earth Sciences says: 'A conservative estimate is that there is enough gas locked away in these ice-like hydrates to double all the known fossil fuel resources of the Earth... that have been used or ever will be.'

Japan and India, which both import vast amounts of fuel, are moving quickly into investigating how soon they can extract the gas from the crystals, the exploitation of which could completely change their economy.

No one is quite sure yet how to harvest the crystals – or, indeed, if they should even be disturbed. Heating them by steam under pressure or dredging up the sea beds could be a recipe for a weather catastrophe of monumental proportions. Burning all those hydrates as fuel could accelerate the process and, as Dr Clennell warns, increase the risk of global warming.

The ice crystals can in fact be disturbed naturally, as, notably, during the last Ice Age 10,000 years ago. Dr Clennell describes the process: 'There is a place off Norway where, because of the sea levels suddenly changing, the gas hydrates there were destabilized. There was a massive landslide, thousands of square kilometres in extent, that slid down the continental slope and generated a massive tsunami.' Boulders from Norway were dumped on the Shetlands.

Such tsunamis as this ancient one may be generated on a far more dramatic scale than those caused by earthquakes or undersea volcanoes. The problem is that until recently no one had ever connected the more massive tsunamis with mud slides caused by a huge upsurge of gas from hydrate crystals disturbing the sediment. In some places, such as the Black Sea and the Andaman Sea, the upsurge of gas can cause mud islands to suddenly rise up out of the sea. Often these towering, bubbling masses are hit by lightning, illuminating a lurid, almost primeval scene which people wrongly identify as volcanic in origin. One mud island that famously appeared off Trinidad caused great panic and alarm when labelled a volcano. Like all these mud islands, it was short-lived, strong tides and currents destroying it in a matter of months.

Another danger is that masses of gas escaping to the surface could cause ships to suddenly lose buoyancy and sink. This could happen at any time, anywhere – and it is quite possible that mysterious disappearances of shipping on fine days in calm seas were the result of such gas escapes. In other parts of the world, agitated waters where gas hydrates escape and bubble upwards are known to local fishermen as good spots to fish – because marine life feeds on the methane, with great shoals of fish at the top end of the food chain. There is plenty of evidence to show that gas escapes explosively from the sea bed. Sonar images of the sea floor from all around the world show pock marks and enormous craters where gas has burst violently upwards.

The world seems to absorb the natural occurrences of escaping gas hydrates – but we cannot know what would happen if we did indeed dredge millions of acres of the bottom of the oceans. The ocean floor is at the bottom of a very complex food chain; the results could be that we might even end up with no fish in the sea – in addition to the damage to the climate. Our planet is a very finely balanced weather machine. It is this delicate balance between sun, sea and sky that makes our life on Earth possible. The ocean is the great regulator, a savings bank for solar energy – without it, the world would experience such harsh extremes of temperature that life would not be possible. The water cycle and its properties are of primary importance.

The energy stored in the oceans is phenomenal. The heat capacity of 3 cubic metres of sea water is equivalent to that of the whole atmosphere above it. The North Atlantic Ocean alone transports heat northwards at a rate equivalent to 30,000 times the output of all UK power stations. If the weather were a machine, the oceans would be its flywheel.

The extremes of the Earth's climate are tempered by the slow circulation of the seas between the Equator and the poles. Ocean currents distribute heat and cold over thousands of miles, which compensate for both the fierce heat of the sun and the unending cold of the ice caps. The regulating thermostat of ocean currents carries hot equatorial water towards the poles and returns cold water back to the Equator.

An important thermostat is found on the edge of the Arctic Circle between Norway and Greenland. The Arctic is almost completely surrounded by land but there are just two small gaps – the Bering Strait between Asia and North America and the gap between Norway and Greenland where there is an underwater ledge just 300 or so feet deep.

The northern ocean thermostat acts like this: the warm Atlantic sweeps over the Greenland ledge into the colder Arctic; the ice cap melts and its moisture falls as snow on the lands which surround it – building up into glaciers, which in turn travel down to the sea where they become icebergs. Cold winds, relieved of their moisture, blow from the advancing glaciers, drying up fertile lands into deserts. As moisture is locked up in all this ice, the sea levels fall and expose the Greenland ledge – which acts like a giant thermostat. The Arctic is now cut off from the warmer Atlantic and freezes over. The glaciers, no longer fed by snow, begin to melt. The ocean level rises and the cycle starts again.

You can see the effects of the oceans if you compare places near the sea where there is little difference between winter and summer temperatures to places in the middle of the continents where seasonal extremes are much larger (such as London and Moscow, San Francisco and Chicago). The ocean currents share with the atmosphere the task of moving heat away from the Equator towards the poles. The water is cooled on the polar regions, sinks to the sea bed and returns towards the Equator completing the circuit. Even at the Equator the water at the sea floor 5 kilometres deep is close to zero degrees Celsius. This cooling results in a river of sub-zero water flowing southwards past the UK at a rate equivalent to 50 Amazon rivers (1 million tons per second).

It is the atmosphere which acts directly upon the ocean. It receives mostly pure water vapour through evaporation, leaving most of the salts in the sea, thus increasing its relative salinity and making it heavier. Water in the air is also heavy; the dense, saturated atmosphere brings variable pressure to bear on the surface of the sea, which depresses under these areas of high pressure – and springs up to compensate in other areas under atmospheric lows. This force helps create the winds which grip the surface of the ocean, whipping it into waves and driving the currents around the world, redistributing the hot and cold waters. It is an endless circle, a pattern of global scale.

The oceans' effect on the temperature and humidity of the atmosphere is far greater than the transfer of heat from air to sea. It takes 3,000 times as much heat to warm water as it does to heat the same amount of air. Or, looking at it the other way around, heat lost by a cubic metre of water is enough to heat 3,000 cubic metres of air. This demonstrates very clearly how the ocean affects the very air above it. Where air is cold, pressure tends to be high; where it is warm it tends to be low. These belts of high and low pressure affect and shape the great winds that circle the planet – and these in turn further help to regulate the weather.

High pressure over the oceans plays a major part in controlling the weather in surrounding lands and it is also the birthplaces of most of the dominant wind systems of the world. The trade winds, so beloved of sailors on the old sailing ships, originate in high pressure belts of the Northern and Southern Hemispheres.

But in winter, when the sea is warmer than the land, huge belts of low pressure develop which attract fast-moving cyclonic storms. We have all seen these great swirls on the television weather maps.

In the tropics, where the sun heats the water, the sea finds its most violent expression. Vast quantities of sea water evaporate, forming huge and unstable storm clouds. Sea and sky come together to spawn hurricanes. It's a brutal genesis, disorganized and ill-defined, but in the humid chaos of these tropical skies competing thunderstorms are drawn to each other, pooling their strength and soaring skywards. Up to 200,000 million tons of water vapour evaporate from the sea every twenty-four hours. Resulting cloud banks are deflected by the Earth's rotation into tight, spinning coils. In simplistic terms: in the Northern Hemisphere, the wind circles anti-clockwise around a low pressure zone and clockwise around a high; and vice versa in the Southern Hemisphere. On the whole, in the Northern Hemisphere, winds are deflected to the right. Around the central eye, the winds accelerate to over 75 miles an hour.

In the Pacific, a hurricane is called a typhoon. The area from Hawaii to Guam is known as Typhoon Alley, so beloved of old John Wayne movies. Typhoon Paca was one of the rarest: it had two eyes and one gust of 236 miles an hour was recorded – an unconfirmed world record.

THE WIND FROM THE SEA

A hurricane, hitting the shore, brings together all the stupendous force of the wide oceans and dumps it on to land. The energy released in a single day would provide the entire United States with electricity for six months.

In south Asia, they are known as cyclones – but whatever the name, they can be killers on a horrifying scale. In Bangladesh alone, in the last twenty-five years, tropical cyclones have claimed over half a million lives. On just a single day, 12 November 1970, a 50-foot-high wave generated by a cyclone heading into the Ganges Delta took more lives than any other wave in history: up to half a million people were drowned; one low-lying island alone lost all 20,000 of its inhabitants.

Unlike tornadoes or lightning, hurricanes are not fleeting phenomena. In the United States and the Caribbean islands, where most hurricanes make landfall, there's time to track them, to watch them grow, to try and guess their final destination. Each hurricane has its own personality and each gets its own name.

The National Hurricane Centre in Miami has responsibility for keeping a hurricane watch over both the Pacific and the Atlantic. The Atlantic alone is a hurricane breeding ground of some 4 million square miles. Florida, the home of the centre, is in the firing line for Atlantic-born hurricanes, but by 1992 no major hurricane had made landfall there for over thirty years. If Florida had grown complacent, one August weekend that year would change everything.

On 17 August 1992 winds in a depression off West Africa accelerated to 40 miles an hour, making what was named Andrew the first tropical storm of the season. At first, it looked harmless, meandering aimlessly in mid-Atlantic. But unexpectedly, it took off, its internal winds rising above 75 miles an hour – Hurricane Andrew was born.

In the Miami suburb of South Dade, Emma Lou Davis recalls: 'The police came and said everybody had to evacuate before the storm gets here. But we laughed. We didn't think it was going to be that bad. I didn't believe it.'

Many people in Miami were disbelieving when hurricane warnings were given. While nearly a million fled their homes, many others stayed put. But, as Andrew

headed due west straight for them, the city high-rises and causeways suddenly seemed very vulnerable. It was the people of South Dade, Miami's sprawling south suburbs, who took the brunt of what was to follow.

Stan Goldenberg, the hurricane research scientist with the National Weather Service, was torn between his wife who was expecting their fourth child that day and his other children at home. Fortunately, the baby was born before the storm, and Goldenberg could sit the storm out with his children, crammed between mattresses in the hallway of their home in South Dade. Despite his knowledge of storms, it was far worse than anything he had anticipated. 'My kids were just crying and screaming. I kept saying it's okay. We were terrified. With all the scientific understanding I had of everything, with all my faith – it was an incredible experience. We certainly wondered if we were going to live. We were in about the most terrifying situation we could imagine in the worst part of the storm... pinned under the walls all night... they fell on top of us.'

Emma Lou Davis, who had decided it was all a fuss about nothing, went to bed. Then the house started to vibrate: 'When I woke up I heard something. I know it wasn't an airplane and I know it wasn't a train. It was so frightening. It sounded like the end of the world. It sounded like an earthquake. The wind looked like crying. When I went to the bathroom, the window blew out. I ran back and got my children and we went into the little bathroom. It was too tiny, we couldn't hardly take breath. But everything was squeaking and rocking, everything all up in the air.'

Michael Shoemaker, also of South Dade, achieved an ambition – he looked straight

Above Hurricane Andrew in action in Miami, Florida, in August 1992, clearing the streets of people and vehicles, making it resemble a ghost town taken over by violent winds and rain.

Opposite A satellite view, showing whirling winds and the vortex-like shape of clouds formed in a hurricane.

up to heaven through the eye of the storm. He was scared to death: 'The roof was gone and I was looking up. I could see the inside of the wall. I could see the clouds boiling. It was like dark smoke... there was starlight coming down through the eye. There was absolutely nothing blocking the light from the stars; Southern Florida was blacked out. I got this shot to God, straight up to the heavens. All the stars were there, all the light coming down. I told my mother, we were not going to die. I said, try and be strong. I don't think hurricanes are fun any more.'

Stan Goldenberg and his family survived, as did Emma Lou Davis and Michael Shoemaker, but like 50,000 other families they lost their homes that night. Hurricane Andrew, born of water sucked up out of the ocean off Africa, was to be one of the costliest national disasters to hit the United States, costing fifty-eight lives and an estimated over $35 billion dollars' worth of damage. There was so much damage to the infrastructure that for the first time in the modern history of the US, local government ceased to function. For four days in Florida there was a spiralling down of society into a kind of anarchy. The elements had revealed the fragility of the civilization we take for granted.

Andrew had also permitted a glimpse of a terrifying natural phenomenon: the damage patterns revealed the presence of colossal downdraughts, each with the force of a tornado, carried within the eye wall of the hurricane itself.

Hurricanes have always visited the United States regularly. In 1900 the city of Galveston was the richest in the state of Texas, a bustling, vigorous port known as the New York of the South, dealing with thousands of ships a year. But crucially, the highest point in Galveston was only 9 feet above sea level. The hurricane of September 1900 brought a 20-foot storm surge, killing 6,000 people in what was the United States' greatest ever weather disaster. Yet, within a handful of years, exactly the same scenes were to be witnessed in Corpus Christi, Texas, by a young boy called Bob Simpson.

'That very day when I was only six years old, it showed me what a terrible destructive power a hurricane can bring in. Houses swirling around in the stream, citizens on their side, rolling around in the currents... a few sad things... people trying to hold on to logs and the logs would thump them on the head and they would disappear. So much destruction. Hundreds and hundreds of people lost their lives and those that lived, lost their property. The town was in a position of desperation.'

Showing the damage in Dade County, South Florida, in the aftermath of Hurricane Andrew, the most violent and costly tropical storm to hit Florida in 60 years. Damage estimates were put at $35 billion, with 200,000 people left homeless in 200 kph winds that turned buildings into matchsticks, tossed boats ashore and uprooted trees.

Bob Simpson grew up to run the National Hurricane Centre in Miami. Passionate about hurricanes, he made the first ever research flight into the eye of a hurricane: 'As you approach the storm you see the first giant squall line of the spiral rain bands... We got a nice pop or two as we went through... but it didn't last very long... as you reached the eye wall it had something of an elevator effect. All of a sudden the plane is rising, rising, rising, because of the uprush of air in the eye wall... If the pilot doesn't aim the plane down you rise thousands of feet... the eye itself, suddenly it's smooth as glass.'

WATERSPOUT

The waterspout is a miniature demonstration of the weather machine in action: sea and sky in partnership, as seen in 1967 when researchers flew an aircraft right through the middle. It looks solid, but they experienced at first hand the exhilaration of buffeting into circular vapour clouds spinning downwards from storm clouds at 130 miles an hour. The sea fills just the bottom 20 feet or so; but it's still a scary monster, soaring up to 3,000 feet and able to dump thousands of tons of water on to the decks of a ship in its path.

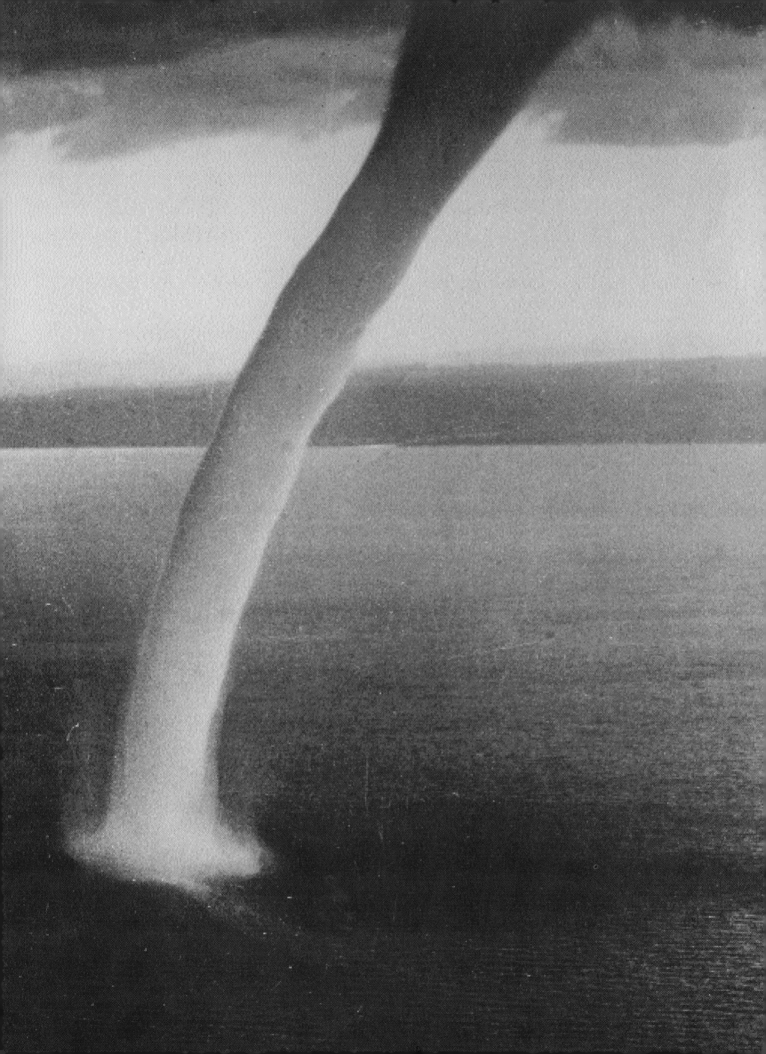

Famous sailors over the years have encountered waterspouts, and some have hoped to escape them by 'breaking' the wall and allowing it to collapse – like round-the-world navigator and map-maker William Dampier, who took pot shots at them with an ageing blunderbuss. Even so, there are no records of ships actually capsizing when a waterspout runs into them.

One of the most impressive waterspouts, 'The Great Waterspout of 1896', occurred one hot August day off Martha's Vineyard, Massachusetts. It just seemed to stand there, nearly six miles off shore – a gigantic black column of wind and water 144 feet thick, towering over 3,500 feet high with a parent cloud hovering thousands of feet above. Veteran old tars watching from the shore described it as the most perfectly formed waterspout they had seen in all their seafaring years. And, unlike the Gloucester Serpent – also spotted off Massachusetts in the nineteenth century (see page 187) – photographers were on hand to record this phenomenon. The spout appeared not once but three times, almost surreal in the middle of a calm blue sea on a bright sunny day, so silent it could have been a mirage.

A waterspout appeared in more recent memory off Miami, which caused a great deal of excitement and was captured on television for everyone to see. Waterspout chaser Jim Lushine was on hand. His love affair with this phenomenon has lasted for over thirty years. 'The fascination with the waterspout is its beauty and intensity... Miami is the waterspout capital of the United States – we've had more here than practically any other place in the world – but it is unusual to see a waterspout come right over the downtown skyline.'

Lushine describes the conditions required for tornadic waterspouts to form as being contrasts in air masses between cold and warm air, with jet streams in place. The clouds that help them are super cell thunderstorms. These do what ordinary thunderstorms don't do – which is rotate. The tornadic waterspout actually drops down from cloud height to hit the surface of the sea like the tail of a dog going down to the ground. At sea level the rotation vacuums water up to a height of about 20 feet; the rest of the moisture is in the towering spiral of water vapour.

David Weir and Christian Dam were on a boat under the harbour causeway, preparing to rig a mast on a sailboat, when they realized that the Miami waterspout, which was being filmed by a TV crew, was heading straight for them. Watching the drama unfold on camera, people saw that the waterspout was white with the light, but from a different angle it looked more menacing. Dave and Christian scrambled out of the way just in time as the boat was lifted up and smashed against the harbour wall. They made a rash decision to run for their van. But the beast was now rotating at 110 miles per hour. Moving faster than a man could run, it went straight for the van with the boat's 800-pound mast and rigging on top. When it hit the van, it lifted off the mast as if it were a stick of candy, carrying it away.

'We kinda made a stupid decision. Debris was falling all around us... tarpaper, wood... you can't see anything at that point, you've lost sight of the funnel so to speak...'

As suddenly as it came, the spout vanished, leaving at least two exhilarated witnesses with a tale to tell.

Opposite Waterspouts used to terrify the ancients, and they're still pretty scary when encountered in full whirling action. A miniature demonstration of the weather machine at work, they look solid and as if they are rising from the sea – but in fact they are made from gusts of wind spiralling downwards. The suction sucks up sea water in just the first 20 feet or so – the rest is vapour.

EL NIÑO – THE BOY CHILD

El Niño can cause floods on one side of the world, and a drought on the other. This water hole is now full again – but the bones of dead cattle in the Outback, Australia, show the results of El Niño.

Storms, hurricanes and waterspouts, while severe, soon pass. But El Niño is a permanent part of our lives and has been for thousands – possibly millions – of years. Born in the far western Pacific, its effects encircle the globe, influencing and changing the weather every few years on a massive scale.

El Niño means the boy child and it's at Christmas time that this phenomenon tends to occur. The tropical Pacific covers one-third of our planet. Off the coast of Peru, an upwelling of cooler subsurface waters in the eastern Pacific brings cool seas loaded with nutrients. Fish, particularly anchovy, follow these seas, and birds feed on the fish; the skies and the seas are full of animals and birds. Cold currents are dry; with little rain – much of Peru is a desert. But sometimes, a great slab of warm water equal in size to the United States suddenly moves across the Pacific from its home base off New Guinea, pushing aside the cold currents off South America. The fish disappear, the birds fly elsewhere – and in Peru, the desert blooms.

In normal years these warm waters persist for only a few weeks; but in some years, mysteriously, the El Niño effect spirals dramatically and lasts for many months. Wherever the warm waters go, rain follows. On the coast of Peru, the El Niño of 1983 brought rain for almost six months, washing away bridges and causing landslides. Ironically, while both North and South America were flooded out, and hundreds of thousands drowned in China when great rivers burst their banks, the opposite happens in Australia and Africa: here there are severe droughts. In Melbourne in 1983 people choked on swirling dust storms; in New Guinea a severe *frost* followed by chronic drought led to hundreds dying of starvation; in Indonesia uncontrollable forest fires have bought smog to vast regions – while in Africa farmers went to extraordinary lengths to prevent an ecological disaster by feeding the wildlife. As several farmers said: 'Africa without rhinos and elephants would not be Africa.'

El Niño, which occurs every two to seven years, has a remarkable effect on temperature, storms and rainfall everywhere on Earth. Meteorologist Professor William Gray also discovered that in El Niño years there were fewer hurricanes. Nobody has quite figured out yet the intense effect it has on the climate. Scientists believe it is a kind of pressure valve that stops our planet from getting too hot.

But in 1997, for some reason, El Niño was recalcitrant. It came swaggering in bigger and more aggressively than ever before and lingered, reluctant to leave the Christmas party. In California, double the normal rain fell. All of a sudden, El Niño was news. People who had never heard of it before were telephoning the TV stations to ask what was going on. CBS weatherman Steve Rambo is in the weather business; he's not a magician. He can spot an El Niño storm in the making – he can even tell you where it is headed – but what he cannot tell you is if you are to be the weather machine's next victim.

Laguna Beach in southern California is the perfect winter playground; with mountains on one side and sea on the other, it's one of the favourite retreats of

El Niño brings high storm waves to California.

Original Beaufort Scale of wind speeds and force

Beaufort number	Description	Wind speed (mph)
0	calm	less than 1
1	light air	1–3
2	light breeze	4–7
3	gentle breeze	8–12
4	moderate breeze	13–18
5	fresh breeze	19–24
6	strong breeze	25–31
7	moderate gale	32–38
8	fresh gale	39–46
9	strong gale	47–54
10	whole gale	55–63
11	storm	64–75
12	hurricane	more than 75

everyone from movie stars to well-off retired people. In 1997 El Niño struck and torrential rains seemed to dissolve the mountains into liquid mud. The Sarabias' world was about to be turned upside-down by a torrent of mud.

Ivonne Sarabia was at home with her parents and her baby sister Tiffany, when a mudslide swept the whole house away. Ivonne was frantic. She ran screaming to rescue workers, looking for her baby sister everywhere, convinced the worst had happened. Then she saw Tiffany in the arms of a fireman, safe and well, though very muddy. Later, Ivonne was reunited with her parents in a hospital. She had lost her home but her family, albeit battered and bruised, were together again. Ivonne's El Niño nightmare was at an end.

Along the coastline, storms driven by El Niño whipped up the sea into huge waves and turned the normally friendly beaches of Southern California into a wild and unfamiliar landscape, Mary Buckley felt her retirement home was her Eden, a place she could trust. Her home, in a small retirement community, was very close to the ocean. She certainly didn't expect the roof of her house to fall in – literally. When massive waves were driven in by the El Niño effect there was no gently shelving beach to dissipate the action of the waves: they came straight for the houses.

Mary describes what happened next:

'*The waves had been hitting for about two weeks, it was pretty intense. I had been getting up about an hour before high tide every morning, watching. I got up [this day] about five o'clock because I heard the waves hitting the windows and high tide wasn't until seven. Then I heard a roar – and I thought this one's really going to get us. When it hit, it hit the top of my roof and wrote the whole hall in, in one big piece. The glass didn't break until it hit the floor and the furniture. It happened so fast that you didn't have time to be afraid. The waves just kept coming for an hour... but you move. You wade through the water, grab your purse and your phone... and out.*'

Before calling at Mary's the storm had travelled a thousand miles across the Pacific, bringing with it a huge area of low pressure. Mary explains its two weeks of unusual ferocity by saying the ocean was very angry. It was a child, El Niño, having a temper tantrum.

THE GREAT FLOOD

On the other side of the world, no one would ever accuse the weather as having a temper tantrum when the saturated monsoon winds come in late May, for the monsoon is a giver of life, the lifeblood of over half the world's populations, bringing much-needed rains to an overheated and parched continent. In the hot cities of Bombay and Calcutta the talk is of nothing else but when will the monsoon come? People who have grown listless in the 100-degree heat for weeks on end crave its cooling powers. In the paddy fields, farmers pray for it.

Monsoon rains are the heaviest on earth, triggering violent, unpredictable thunderstorms that seem to roll all the way from the Indian Ocean to the Himalayan Mountains. They are not single, raging storms like a hurricane or cyclone – but a pulsating wavelike air mass that moves from the sea to the land, and back again as the winds change direction. Monsoon winds are so powerful, sucking up so much salty sea water as evaporation, that an astonishing 3,000 tons of salt a year are carried in from the Indian Ocean and dumped into Sambhar Salt Lake in northern India some 400 miles away.

Nature performs a dangerous balancing act; without the monsoon India, that lush green continent, would be as dry as the Arabian peninsula. But if it rains too much, floods cause massive destruction. Much of Bangladesh lies at sea level. It can be devastated by the power of the monsoon; the torrential rains trigger flooding when the great sacred rivers, the Ganges, the Brahmaputra and the Megna, overfill, spilling their excess towards the sea. Each year 70 per cent of the country is flooded, but to the farmers it is a way of life. They depend on the flood waters from the mineral-rich plains and hills replenishing worn soils with alluvial nutrients. It is not a free gift, however. There is a price.

In this part of the world, the two cyclone seasons are more certain than the hurricane season is in the United States. Often in Bangladesh the news of impending doom for millions of people comes in the shape of a low-key radio announcement. These are desperately poor people, forced to live on low-lying chars or silt islands because they have nowhere else to go.

Beaufort the Man

Many people have heard of the Beaufort scale (invented 1805); but few know that it was devised by Sir Francis Beaufort (1774–1857) – a tough old sea dog who joined the British Navy as a boy of thirteen, seeing action almost at once in the Battle of the Glorious First of June against the French during their Revolutionary War. Always in the thick of the fighting, in just one naval engagement he was wounded by three sword cuts and sixteen musket balls. In the course of a long life at sea, he experienced the wind in all its many moods, from the Etesian – a Mediterranean wind that rises every August and blows gently in the same direction for forty days – to the fierce winds that blow ships hundreds of miles off course around Cape Horn, the tip of South America.

Had Beaufort experienced the world's most consistent windiest place – Commonwealth Bay on the George V coast of Antarctica, where winds have been recorded at 200 mph – then he would have had to readjust his scale. As it is, in the light of such strong winds, the Beaufort scale now goes up to an incredible 17 – although the increase is little used and rarely shown. Beaufort went on to become a rear-admiral and Hydrographer of the Navy, devising many charts and weather systems still in use today, including the Ship's Code and Decode Book which shows a system of letters to explain the weather.

Main picture A family drifts in a boat past flooded houses in Bhuapur, Bangladesh, looking for survivors in the aftermath of monsoon floods.

Inset The 1998 monsoon floods in Bangladesh and India left more than 30 million people homeless. Here, villagers moving to higher ground collect sacks of rice and the few possessions they have managed to salvage as rising flood waters overwhelm their homes.

Like the waterspout, the cyclone feeds on water that is warm (27 degrees or above) but on a far more massive scale. It's a destructive explosion of energy but, like El Niño, it helps to keep the weather machine in balance.

Bangladesh can ill afford cyclones because of a series of unique factors: a big tide of at least 15 feet; a funnelling coast configuration which increases the height of the waves; and low, flat terrain. The frequent tropical storms produce an average of one major cyclone every three years. The areas worst affected tend to be in the east around Chittagong and Cox's Bazaar.

The worst cyclone in living memory was in 1970 – up to half a million people drowned when whirling winds drove the sea before them and on to the land. The flood of 1991 was worse, affecting twice as many people and destroying four times as many houses, but it killed fewer people because the construction of storm shelters limited deaths. The 1991 cyclone was detected some four days beforehand, as it formed a depression over the Bay of Bengal. With maximum wind speeds of 140 miles an hour, accompanied by 21-foot-high waves, bamboo-frame houses did not stand a chance. Nearly every family had a member who was swept away. Because of the state of chaos and communication problems, it was two weeks before some villages received help.

In 1970, Bhanu Bibi was bringing up her first family and remembers that far-off night in November. As she crouched in fear with her children, she turned to God to save them. 'I prayed and prayed and made promises to God. I promised to give 100 taka to Mecca if he saved my house and children.' But it was not to be. One of her daughters was swept into a date tree full of thorns. 'I saw her body, all bloody. I was so weak I couldn't tell she was dead. So many children were washed away. They were found dead in the fields. Floating like fish... dead.'

Mud building up in the Ganges Delta is literally creating new land. As soon as the sea drains away a new rice crop will be transplanted to the emerging mud flats. Of course the tide will return but this is a hardy variety of rice that can withstand a few dunkings in salt water before the char is established and the tide can't reach it any more. Meanwhile, provided nothing too devastating happens, the island will grow every minute of every day, gradually rising up out of the sea.

The wave that devastated Bhanu Bibi's family reached 30 feet. The water that rose behind it drowned the frail bamboo houses built on stilts and drove the first survivors into the upper branches of the few trees that were still standing. The water stayed for two hours, while people held on desperately. Then the cyclone wind came howling in at speeds of over 70 miles an hour, tearing everyone from their fragile handholds in the branches.

As the sea sped towards Romoni Mahon's house, he lifted his four-year-old son in his arms and headed for the nearest big tree. He made the right decision to try to climb above the water, but it was not enough. 'Three big waves hit me. I looked to the East and said, "God, you save your child. I can't do any more." Then I let go my son. As I swam away, I felt something grabbing my shirt tail. I realized afterwards that my son must have washed back to me and was trying to hang on to me. The pain will never go away. If we were rich people we wouldn't live here.'

In this part of the world, as long as there is light enough to see, the work of gathering seedlings continues. The next morning after the storm waters have gone down, the clumps from the newly established rice fields will be transplanted to the new land that just a few hours ago was the sea bed. All this land costs lives.

Bhanu Bibi spells it out: 'The sea took everything. It took the children and it will take them away again.'

She is right. The monsoon will return as surely as night follows day – as demonstrated by the deluge during 1998. For more than two months during the summer a combination of unusually heavy monsoon rain and flooded rivers flowing down from the mountains in India caused the Brahmaputra and the Ganges rivers to overfill. Abnormally high tides pushed inland by monsoon winds added to the disaster, leading to what Prime Minister Sheikh Hasina described as 'the most prolonged natural disaster in the country', with more than 25 million people left homeless or stranded. Despite extensive sand-bagging along the dikes, over half of the capital of Dhaka was under water for weeks. (In neighbouring Assam, India, where floods devastated 2.2 million acres of farmland, widespread starvation resulted.)

Sea fog, which is hazardous to shipping, usually forms where cold currents meet warm ones. There are many collisions in thick fog, despite ships blowing their horns while the warning light of a lighthouse is rendered useless.

SEA FOG

Where warm currents meet cold currents, fogs occur. Some of the thickest fogs occur off Japan, while California is notorious for long periods of mist that roll in off the sea and linger for weeks on end. But the constant, mournful sound of ships' horns sounding through the thick blanket of almost solid fog that lies over the Grand Banks, where cold Labrador Current meets warm Gulf Stream water, is a reminder of just how dangerous this area can be.

In the summer of 1980, deckhands Dave Mitchell and Alan Creaser were returning to Lunenburg from Georges Bank when the sea overtook their wooden scallop dragger, *Margaret Jane*. The men were on deck putting gear away when a much larger steel boat broke out of the fog and rammed them.

Dave said the fog was so thick he didn't even see the other ship at first, he just saw white water and knew something big was approaching.

The collision was bad enough in this area notorious for accidents, but it need not have been a disaster until the bigger vessel began to back out of the hole it had made. Within seconds, the deck of the *Margaret Jane* was awash and the unthinkable happened – so fast that the crew didn't have enough time to panic. They threw a liferaft over the side and, as the ship went down, had to leap for it.

It took eighty seconds for the sea to claim the *Margaret Jane*, something that will live for ever in the minds of all who were there. Four men drowned that day. The youngest was a student who was saving up by working during the vacation to buy a high-tech sail boat. The oldest was a man who was about to retire; this was to be his last trip. It *was* his last trip – but not in the way he had imagined.

For Dave Mitchell and Alan Creaser, the accident – the latest in a long line of accidents for shipping in that area – was the final straw. Dave took a year off fishing. When he went back, ghosts returned to haunt him: 'I never slept much because when you are fishing around on Georges Bank you are with other boats and of course you have horns... you are blowing the horn and give your signal... but I was on edge for a year or so. It took a while to really kinda get the fear out of my mind.'

As for Alan, the accident was enough to persuade him that life at sea was not for him. He bought a bar in Lunenburg and never looked back.

Both captains were held responsible for the accident; this time, nobody blamed the sea.

THE TREASURE FLEETS

No one would imagine that diving for wrecks would have anything to do with the weather – but often it was the weather that put some of the richest treasure ships in the world at the bottom of the sea. The area that has more treasure ships than any other is the Caribbean, notorious for hurricanes.

In the sixteenth century, navigation to the New World and the Caribbean was a mystery. It took many years for navigators to discover that the easiest route across the Atlantic was not the most obvious one. The winds and currents moved in a circle, north to south in the east and south to north in the west. Spanish galleons sailed south of Spain to the Canaries and then headed west towards Brazil. From there, they turned north and entered into the Caribbean at the Dragon's Mouth – between Trinidad and Grenada.

Waiting for them at Portobello on the Gulf of Darien were vast piles of treasure – treasure that had been tortured out of the natives of South America, and treasure that had been carried halfway across the world from the Philippines by huge galleons. This was transported across the narrow isthmus on the backs of mules, to – quite literally

Treasure galleons such as these Portuguese carracks carried vast amounts of treasure from the New World to the Old. Many of them were lost to pirates and to tropical storms in the Caribbean, where the treasure still lies at the bottom, awaiting discovery.

A diver off the Bahamas – graveyard of many 16th- and 17th - century treasure ships wrecked in tropical storms and hurricanes.

– wait in iron chests in the bars and streets of Portobello while the crews made merry (as Drake and Henry Morgan found to their benefit and amusement) until the fleets came to carry it home.

Home lay northwards. Navigators had learned that there was a mysterious current that swept them past the Bahamas and Florida, past mainland America – until they could safely turn east, homeward bound for Spain. And because the Spanish, a military-minded people, kept to a very strict timetable, they refused themselves any leeway for the weather, not even for hurricanes. Ships often disappeared without a trace – and it wasn't always down to pirates like Drake and Morgan. Sometimes a small group of castaways were picked up to tell what happened; often their ships were overcome by a storm, as in the case of the *Maestro Juan*, whose fate was a mystery for a year – until some of her crew were spotted on the lonely cay where they had survived by drinking turtles' blood.

From 1500 to 1820 some 49 billion dollars' worth of treasure crossed the Atlantic from the New World. It has been estimated from the records in Seville that about 5 per cent was lost to storms, pirates and bad luck. One of the worst disasters occurred in the Windward Passage off Haiti – at that time called Santa Domingo – on 1 July 1505. Laden with Aztec and Inca gold, silver from their mines and pearls from Catalina, the flagship *El Dorado* was commanded by Bobadilla – the man who had imprisoned Christopher Columbus some two years earlier on some trumped-up charge. After Columbus was released, their paths crossed at the end of June at Santa Domingo. Columbus, a canny and experienced mariner, knew from the signs that a hurricane was imminent.

He wrote: 'I warned both Señor Torres and Bobadilla, but they were scornful of my superior seamanship, dismissing it as nothing compared with theirs. And had I not discovered these very islands through which they sailed?'

Four days later, in the Mona Passage, one of the worst storms in history hit the treasure fleet. For twelve hours, cyclonic winds and mountainous waves battered the flotilla. Many of the ships were thrown upon the shores around the passage. Many more were swept towards Tortuga, others to the Bahamas. Twenty-seven heavily laden caravels and over 500 lives were lost – including that of Bobadilla, the man who wouldn't listen to sense from a master mariner.

This area of sea became known as the Silver Shoals – and the passage through the islands, Hurricane Alley. Numerous wrecks lie in the shallow waters, but tides and currents have covered many of them with sand. The weather too, can be very cruel; and divers talk of sharks and even sea snakes. It is only in recent years that salvage experts, such as Carl Fismer of the Spanish Main Treasure Company, have been able to go down to the sea bed to dredge up the treasures of the past. Researching the treasure ships and their manifestos is not easy; it has been estimated that 90 per cent of the careful documents from this period stored in the Library at Seville have never been read.

For Captain Carl Fismer, treasure hunting is a way of life. Artefacts from previous salvage operations adorn his home in the Florida Keys, from pieces of eight from a Spanish colonial galleon to a skull picked up from the ocean floor. The area where he is looking for treasure is the Hogsty Reef – known to early mariners as 'Dragons Teeth'; it is towards the southern end of the Bahamian chain. So far, the team have located twenty-four wreck sites but not a great deal of real treasure in the form of pieces of eight or gold bars.

Hurricane Alley is still guarding its secrets.

the big chill

Ice islands seven miles long; vodka made from icebergs; a sea where the fatal accident rate is 100 times higher than any other industry in the United States; ice-breakers that crash through vast ice-fields; water that can kill in forty-five seconds; iced ships that are so heavy they capsize in minutes – ice and cold water are our bitter foes.

ICE

Our world begins and ends in ice. In the north, it is a cap, up to 50 metres thick in winter, floating on the 5,400,000 square miles of the Arctic Sea. In the south, it covers a continent the size of Europe, Antarctica, which its weight has almost totally pushed beneath the sea. Antarctica contains 90 per cent of all the ice on Earth.

The coldness of both regions is extreme. Snow and ice reflect about 80 per cent of the sun's radiation back into space. Temperatures sink far below freezing. The coldest temperature ever recorded on Earth was at Russia's Vostock station in the Antarctic: minus 89.6 degrees Celsius. The least wind can produce a wind-chill factor. A 50 kilometre-an-hour wind can reduce a temperature of minus 35 degrees C to minus 70 degrees C. Wind-chill sucks heat from the body by constantly conducting heat away from it.

Just as it is the coldest place on Earth, Antarctica also experiences the strongest winds. The katabatic winds are caused by dense, cold air rushing off the polar plateau down to the Antarctic coast and they can achieve velocities of up to 320 kilometres an hour.

Yet all this icy horror, far from disturbing the peace of humanity, protects us. The coldness of these regions keeps frozen the water that would otherwise submerge much inhabited land and acts, via sea currents, as a cooling agent for an over-hot world. The Arctic and Antarctic are only a threat to those people who choose to disturb their pristine, white, empty isolation. Then, like sleeping giant snow leopards, they can wake and roar and bite with icy, sharp teeth.

Both the Arctic and the Antarctic are giant ice factories but much of the Arctic's ice, icebergs apart, is frozen sea water while the greater part of the Antarctic's has been made from snow and is therefore mainly freshwater ice. This is a process that has happened over many millions of years; the slowness yet vastness of the phenomenon is quite staggering, for Antarctica is the driest desert on Earth. The extreme cold forces water vapour out of the air, and annual snowfall on the polar plateau is equivalent to less than 5 centimetres of rain. Nonetheless, the ice of Antarctica contains nearly 70 per cent of the world's fresh water.

The ice flows, due to pressure created by its own weight, from the high interior towards the coast. Here, large slabs break off the ice sheet to form icebergs. Similarly, about 90 per cent of the icebergs of the Arctic have broken off from glaciers along the coasts of Greenland, Northern Baffin Island and Ellesmere Island, glaciers that have been created over the past 20,000 years from packed snow.

Ice has a life of its own. It can be young, middle-aged or old. It has different colours. It can be thick or thinner. It moves, travels, piles into mountainous ridges, cracks into treacherous crevasses, breaks and melds together again, all accompanied by its own eerie noises.

Most of the Arctic Ocean is covered in polar sea ice, frozen sea water, up to 50 metres thick in winter but which may melt down to 2 metres thick in summer when it retracts back to the coastline. Polar ice is usually flat, with raised edges. When the ice begins to thaw, water melts the underside of the edges, creating ragged effects and deep cracks. The season for exploration is after the worst of the Arctic winter and the total darkness of January and February but before the summer melts the polar ice to instability. Whatever the season, a frozen ocean is still subject to twice-daily tidal movements – the strongest of which occur twice a month, after each new and full moon – and currents.

Polar Ice

'On 23rd March we were told by radio that these tidal fluctuations were causing dramatic movements of ice. In less than twenty-four hours an enormous lead of water had opened, a massive 1,000-mile-long gash running northwest to southeast.' The writer is Robert Swan of the eight-man international Icewalk expedition. Swan followed a walk to the South Pole with one to the North in the spring of 1989, to draw attention to the increasing dangers of environmental pollution.

Like walkers before him, he discovered that polar ice is not always flat. At the edge

A dazzling midnight sun shines on the Icewalk team as they follow in the footsteps of Scott. In 1989 Robert Swan and seven others walked to the South Pole to draw attention to environmental pollution.

Most people are familiar with ice sculptures such as elegant swans used at banquets to display fresh food, while huge and elaborate creations are carved at ice festivals around the world. But during World War II, the British government intended carving full-size aircraft carriers out of icebergs. Project Habbakut, suggested by Geoffrey Pyke and given top priority by Prime Minister Winston Churchill, was to shape polar icebergs in exact proportion, then tow them into shipyards where they would be clad in cheap metal. If bombed or torpedoed, they would not sink – they would merely fill with seawater and continue to float.

It was only the dropping of the atom bomb and the end of the war that curtailed the Pyke Plan – or there would have been fully commissioned 'unsinkable' ice-ships at sea. Compare this with the massively built Russian atomic-powered Arctika – a ship designed to defeat ice. The world's most powerful ice-breaker, it can cut through 7-foot-thick ice at 7 miles an hour.

of Ellesmere Island, from where the expedition commenced: 'Arctic pressure ice was like Everest reduced to rubble.'

Once they were on the Arctic Ocean proper: 'We had ski'd for only half an hour when we encountered a huge wall of pressure ice... Soon we lost count. The ridges were taller and closer together the further north we pushed... we were forced to ferry equipment by hand over a series of crevasses... I could see nothing but a living nightmare, an apocalyptic vision of huge ice boulders and pressure ridges stretching as far as the eye could see.'

Ice-breaker

Shipping – even in areas further south such as the Gulf of St Lawrence, 60,000 square miles bordered by Quebec, Newfoundland and Prince Edward Island – has always known about the vagaries of ice, affected by temperature, winds and currents.

To allow goods in and out of the many eastern seaboard and Great Lakes ports, from the largest such as Montreal and Quebec City to the smallest, ice-breaking ships must ply the waters day and night from the first day of the big freeze, when the sea ices over – December or January – to when the spring thaw starts – in May or June. Without these hefty ice-breakers, it is no exaggeration to say that the economy of the region would collapse. The costs of a large ship run at approximately US$27,000 a day: they cannot afford to be marooned in the ice. The ports must get their goods sent in and out.

'Summers here are very beautiful, but the winters can be very harsh. There is no such thing as a typical year. We deal with Mother Nature all the time and every year is different,' says Jean Pierre Dube, master of the *Sir William Alexander*, a Canadian Coast Guard ice-breaker.

Captain Dube's job is to keep traffic moving through the Gulf of St Lawrence, so it is no surprise to find that he is preoccupied with the thickness and condition of ice. He can tell a great deal by simply looking at it: soft new ice is greyish white while older ice is bluer and harder. You can see the sea forming ice crystals on the surface when it starts to freeze over. At this stage it's basically salt water and a grey-white colour. The salt keeps it soft for a while, then as it ages the salt falls through and mixes with the brine of the sea – so that older ice is actually fresh water, which freezes faster at a higher temperature than salt water. Ice here can get so thick that in the harbours and ports it freezes right down to the sea bed – and then there is no getting through. Captain Dube says: 'When you hit old ice, it's almost like concrete, so a ship will actually bounce and stop. It will actually throw you off your feet sometimes.'

According to Captain Dube: '1994 was a particularly bad year. The ice was heavy, denser, thicker. The harder it is, the harder it is to break. You're basically trying to force a lot of steel through three or four feet of solid ice. We have to back up and use brute force to push the ship on and through it.'

Opposite The forecastle of an icebreaker breaking pack ice in the Weddell Sea, Antartica.

In fact, often the ship itself seems to sense the condition of the ice and will find its own way through – seeking a naturally thinner path called 'a ladder'. The captain will put the ship in neutral under these conditions and let it go by itself. It seems to find the easiest way. Ice-breakers are designed to ride over the ice as they cut. The bow of the vessel has a very gentle slope at the water line which is called an ice-breaking knife or bow. The vessel pushes the bar on top of the ice and then the massive weight of all the steel in the hull pushes down and actually breaks the ice, opening up a lane for other ships to pass through. When the ice is very thick, progress is painfully slow; at these times, allowing the ship to roll a little from side to side will crush the ice and allow further penetration – but on the whole, the ice-breakers believe it is better not to force the issue except in an emergency. 'You can't fight the ice' is a general view.

André Maillet, Superintendent of the Icebreaking Program of the Canadian Coast Guard, directs the search for the best way through the ice. Right in the ice field, he uses an electro-magnetic ice-probe, an expensive gadget that looks like a missile, to detect thinner, lighter ice that they can push a way through. He, too, is an expert in ice: 'Saltwater ice begins to form when the water temperature drops below approximately minus 1.9 degrees. As it thickens it moves around. Sheets sometimes power up on each other in rafts and where it starts to get under pressure, it'll form ridges so it looks like a rubble field. About 75 centimetres is what we call a medium first-year ice.'

According to Maillet, the worst kind of ice in southern waters is thick first-year ice. When it's in loose form, where vessels can enter the ice at speed, the chance of them hitting a piece that will cause damage is far greater. The other problem is ice pressure: when ice squeezes against the hull and rudder, violent manoeuvres have to be made in order to free the vessel, so they're more susceptible to rudder damage.

In 1994 – a bad ice year – the entire Gulf was covered with ice under pressure. It created enormous ridges and trapped numerous vessels. The Coast Guard ice-breakers received over 600 requests for assistance from ships stuck in or damaged by ice. Some ships ran out of fuel because they used it up in wild manoeuvres, trying to free themselves.

Maillet says: 'The ridges were caused by northwest winds which really pushed the ice against the land barriers, in some cases 40 feet high. Along one point on the west coast of Newfoundland, where the community was starting to run out of fuel oil and were almost on the verge of shutting down – which would have been disastrous – our ice-breakers took almost ten days to get there.'

A light ice year for this region usually means that the jet stream current is in the area and that the pattern of weather fronts causes constantly shifting winds which stir up the sea and don't allow the ready formation of ice. Ice forms best in calm seas, light winds that do not change direction and, of course, cold temperatures. But in very low temperatures a changing wind might still prevent ice settling.

Weather prediction these days is a precise science. Information from satellites and radar satellites and ice reconnaissance aircraft can regularly forecast where ice will move. If the wind blows in one direction for any length of time, the ice will compress in that direction. What is harder to predict is where the ice will be least deep or tough.

'Where it will start to ease first,' as André Maillet puts it.

So how can a method of doing this be developed?

> *'We listen to ice. Ice under pressure creates an enormous amount of noise, the formation of a ridge gives off a lot of acoustic signals. We listen to the cracking and popping and grinding, then we look at which areas are more sort of noise active – then we can paint a picture of where a pressure is or, more importantly, where pressure isn't.*
>
> *'The ultimate for us would be to receive a good overview of where ice is and at the same time having technology tell us what the thickness is, so right off the bat we know where to send and where not to send ships. Also to determine the areas of pressure to avoid bad ones and have the forecasting tool of how ice is going to move.'*

At least in the Gulf of St Lawrence, ice forms and melts in the same season. The most dangerous type of ice is the kind that survives more than one season melt. The salt water drains out of it and it gets particularly hard. The Coast Guard service gets numerous cases up in the Arctic when they are called to assist ships in distress.

Man in Polar Regions...

If ships find Arctic ice difficult to cope with, humans certainly ought to keep well away. Journeying by foot on such a frozen sea is only done by forcing human bodies to endure a climate to which they have never adapted. As Robert Swan explains:

> *'Water is the main problem in Arctic survival. Because the air is so cold, it cannot hold moisture. It is therefore very dry, which means that the body loses as much as a gallon of water a day through the nose and breathing passages as it automatically humidifies the parched incoming air. The result, if you don't take in a lot of fluid... is dehydration – a greater problem in the Arctic than in the Sahara... yet the more you dry out, the less thirsty you feel. Fainting and heart attacks are common; you have to keep forcing yourself to take fluids.'*

You also urinate more at first – the body shuts down peripheral blood vessels to preserve core temperature; the circulatory system therefore reduces and the body gets rid of what it perceives as extra fluid from the blood in the form of urine. This in turn causes salt and potassium loss, which can damage the nerves and muscles at precisely the time when both these will be under strain from depression and exhaustion.

The moving body, in layers of modern, insulated clothes, is like a generator, producing heat which keeps the cold at bay. On the move, travellers may even unzip garments to let extra heat out. The second they stop, halting their human generator, they must remember to zip up again to keep the heat in. Every tiny action – removing

a glove or having a pee – may result in frostbite, faster than even experienced polar travellers realize. When hot drinks freeze while they are being drunk, bare fingers will freeze in five seconds.

The early Arctic explorers, trying to penetrate from the 'outside' in, had the bravado of feeling more civilized than the Inuit. Not for them caribou or seal skin or fur – though the traditional Inuit winter outfit has a thermal value of between eight and twelve 'clo', or appropriate warmth, units. A business suit is rated at one clo. Inactivity or sleep demands about 12 clos; physical effort reduces the need to four or five. The Victorian explorers often relied on woollen uniforms; Sir John Franklin and his men, who all died after losing their ships in 1845, were wearing top hats. The modern venturer into the Arctic is more likely to be equipped with thermal and fleece-lined underwear, full-length pile suits, windproof duvet jackets with hoods, balaclavas, fur hats, several pairs of specially designed gloves and socks and sealskin boots with insoles.

The early explorers came in ships and any number of these ships were crushed in ice. In the summer, the ice seemed to melt enough to penetrate, but under the influence of the wind, floes of ice pile up into hummocks, creating enormous pressure.

Around the edges of the ocean is the pack ice. It is not enormously thick – perhaps a maximum of 2 metres – but the endless movement of the sea beneath the ice breaks it and crushes it together again. Adjoining the land, the ice is termed 'fast', meaning that it is attached firmly to the shore. Pack ice, on the other hand, is never firm. At the height of winter, it covers 451,740 square miles of the ocean.

It was the Norwegian scientist, Fridtjof Nansen, who in 1893 came in a specially strengthened ship, the *Fram*, and survived the ice that had crushed so many earlier ships. He deliberately sailed the *Fram* into the pack ice off the New Siberian islands near where an American ship named the *Jeanette* had been crushed in 1879. The *Fram* could not thereafter control its direction: it was taken with the ice. After nearly three years of drifting across the polar ice field, stuck, the *Fram* emerged safe, northwest of Spitsbergen, confirming what until then had only been suspected: that there is a northwest polar drift of the ice, from the middle of the Siberian coast towards the northeastern tip of Greenland.

The clockwise water circulation of the Arctic Ocean is also strongly affected by the Gulf Stream, or North Equatorial Current. This huge mass of warm water starts in the Caribbean Sea, moves to the Gulf of Mexico, escapes through the Florida Straits and continues at a great depth at about 80 miles per day across the North Atlantic to northern Europe. Its warmth is a

lifeline to all the countries which lie in its path – including the British Isles – for it brings them a temperate climate, often far more temperate than their latitude would allow. The Gulf Stream flows north between Greenland and Norway and cools as it travels. It returns southwards through the Davis Strait, between Greenland and Newfoundland, bearing the icebergs which are such a danger to North Atlantic shipping.

These are the icebergs which have broken away or 'calved' from the ice sheet which covers Greenland and the islands off Canada such as Baffin and Ellesmere. The ice has been formed over many thousands of years from packed snow, almost utterly flattened and compressed into a tremendous hardness. Once an iceberg has calved, it majestically moves away, letting the winds and sea take it along the coasts of Labrador or Newfoundland. Only some 20 per cent of an iceberg at the most is visible above the water line and, especially if it is surrounded by pack ice, which prevents the sea's waves eating away at the base, it can last a long time. The life span of an iceberg averages about two years.

Older icebergs may come from ice that has melted and refrozen, each time losing some air that is trapped inside. Gradually, the ice changes from looking white (the effect of the trapped air) to looking green or a wondrous blue. If this old ice calves an iceberg, it will not float as well as an iceberg full of trapped air; it may be almost completely submerged and even more dangerous to shipping. Its ice is likely to be even harder than that of a 'normal' iceberg.

To the people who encounter them, icebergs are beautiful and dangerous individuals, rather like wild animals. And rather like wild animals, they are studied, tracked and hunted. The Arctic icebergs float in packs along the coast of Labrador, a region often called Iceberg Alley. Most are taken along the Grand Banks but many follow a narrow trail along the coast of Newfoundland under the influence of the Labrador Current.

'You really get the icebergs lining up one after another down through there,' says Alan Ruffman, President of Geomarine Associates of Halifax. 'Of course, they're all approaching the southern edge of the Grand Banks where the transatlantic traffic is.'

When the *Titanic* Hit an Iceberg...

One still, starlit night in April 1912, that transatlantic traffic included the grandest passenger liner ever built, on her very first voyage. Can anyone not know that the magnificent, 'unsinkable' *Titanic* hit an iceberg and sank, with the loss of an extraordinary cross-section of 1,513 lives: the fabulously rich, the poor looking for a new life, men, women, children and babies? That among the many, many mistakes that were made that night were the decisions to travel fast in the dark through a region known to have icebergs, not to heed the radio warning from the nearby *Californian* and not to give the lookouts – who had been told to watch for icebergs – binoculars, so that not until they were barely a minute from the towering berg did they ring out and call their warning?

When the warning came, the ship was put sharply into reverse and steered 'hard astarboard'. The *Titanic* at the last second glided past the iceberg on the starboard

On her maiden voyage in 1912 the *Titanic* hit an iceberg that had strayed far south – and sank spectacularly, going down with lights still blazing and the band still playing.

side. Above the water, it had partly missed it, partly brushed it. Under the water, of course, a prong of hard, hard ice jutted out and raked along the side of the ship for about 300 feet, ensuring that enough of the ship's watertight compartments were simultaneously flooded to guarantee its rapid sinking.

The *Titanic* could still have floated with any two of her sixteen watertight compartments flooded, even with all four of the first five in the bow. Not with all of the first five, however. The bulkhead between the fifth and sixth compartments went only as high as E deck. With the first five flooded, the bow would sink so low that water in the first five must overflow into the sixth. Then to the seventh. And so on. The hidden prong of ice was their guillotine blade.

Alan Ruffman: 'Something the captain didn't know, nobody knew until very recently, is how bloody hard the ice is inside an iceberg.'

Finding out was not a picnic. Recent geophysical testing, by oil companies keen to exploit the resources of oil off Newfoundland without losing oil platforms and men in ice accidents, began in the most Heath-Robinson of ways as engineers began to discover how to handle an iceberg. 'They first tried to put people on top of icebergs off Newfoundland,' explains Ruffman. 'They got the men out there and drilled holes in the icebergs, which began to roll. One of the guys was landed on the iceberg in a survival suit and he says he doesn't remember the 100-foot roll the iceberg took, but he does recall that he ended up 100 feet away. After this experiment, they realized they couldn't land on icebergs that way.'

A more cautious process, tunnelling into wintering icebergs held fast in polar ice, demonstrated that just below the berg's 'skin' of seawater ice, the freshwater ice temperature is between minus 10 and minus 20 degrees Centigrade, the same temperature as the original glacier, and effectively as hard as rock.

With hindsight, Alan Ruffman and others believe that the *Titanic* paradoxically might have done better to hit its iceberg head-on.

'*It would have crunched the bow and caused a huge amount of damage but with the watertight doors closed fewer different compartments might have had water in them. Ships can hit icebergs. The* Ivory Star *hit a little growler head on, producing a huge hole of about 30 feet around the bow, but it only punctured a couple of the water tanks, it didn't go back into the structure of the ship.*

'*The* Arizona *in 1879 did that too and the bow looks like it went straight into a brick wall but the ship made it into St John's and survived.*

'*It was even mentioned in the enquiry that First Officer William Murdoch, steering the ship, might have chosen to go straight into the iceberg. His career would have been dead but he would have saved 1,500 lives. We don't know that, though; to hypothesize on these things is futility. The fact was, the* Titanic *had too close a brush with death and it lost.*'

Futile it may be, but there is another small theory too: that reversing the engines simply did not assist the turn the ship was trying to make. 'If they had simply gone over hard on the wheel,' admits Ruffman, 'it might have missed it. A matter of metres, that was all they needed.'

A matter of meteorology too. Oceanographers are just beginning to investigate what seems to be the cyclical nature of iceberg production. There are heavy and light years; some years very few icebergs are calved and come into Grand Banks, while in other years they travel unusually far south. The intrusion of ice south in 1912 indicates that it was the most exceptional year since 1882. Captain Smith and 1,512 others died because he did not take the iceberg warnings seriously, but his professional experience had not led him to expect icebergs in that position or even perhaps to realize just how much of an iceberg – anything from one-fifth to (with very old icebergs) the whole lot – may lie beneath the surface, a treacherous, craggy, unpredictable, jutting lump, according to how sea water and rain have weathered its shape.

Something else neither Captain Edward Smith nor Thomas Andrews, managing director of Harland & Wolff Shipyard where the *Titanic* had been built, nor Bruce Ismay, managing director of the White Star Line, knew was the nature of the *Titanic*'s one-inch-thick steel.

When, in 1985, marine geologist Robert Ballard with an American–French team found the *Titanic* using side scan sonar, its bow was buried in a 35-foot mud bank. The damage caused by the iceberg could not properly be seen. In 1991 a team of scientists and engineers led by Canadian marine geologist Steve Blasco took down to the 12,612-foot-deep site two submersibles capable of staying at great depths for 20-plus hours.

On one dive, they brought up a small chunk of what looked like part of the hull, a ten-inch-diameter disc with three rivet holes, each an inch-and-a-quarter and, amazingly, with remnants of the original paint. For reasons still not fully understood, the steel was hardly corroded but its edges were jagged, almost as if it were a piece of broken china. Its metallurgical condition, however, was similar to a chunk saved from the ship's construction site in 1911: it was as if they were holding a piece of freshly made *Titanic*.

In 1994, in a Canadian Department of Defense laboratory, a special test was set up with a small strip cut off the edge of the precious chunk. The procedure involved smashing it, in the cause of helping solve the 80-year-old mystery of exactly what happened to the *Titanic*. The test measures brittleness: the strip (called a 'coupon') is fixed on a steel holder before a 67-pound pendulum swings down and thumps against it. The point of contact is connected to electronic instruments that document the force and impact. For comparison, a second coupon, of modern ships' steel, was tested. To simulate the cold conditions of the night of 14 April 1912, both pieces were immersed in a bath of alcohol at 29 degrees Fahrenheit (between minus one and minus two degrees Centigrade).

When the pendulum hit the modern steel, it thumped it into a 'V' and it was stopped in its tracks. When it hit the *Titanic* sample, it made a sharp 'ping', barely slowed and continued its trajectory. The pieces of the sample snapped instantly in two and flew across the room.

Further analysis confirmed that the *Titanic* was built of exceptionally brittle steel, manufactured with a sulphur content high even for those days. 'It's full of sulphide inclusions. It would never get out of a shipyard today,' said Duncan Ferguson of the Canadian team. When the ship hit the iceberg, the hull plates were not just dented. They fractured. The concept of brittle fracture was not understood at that period nor how much more brittle steel became in cold conditions. 'But,' said Ken Karis Allen, the metallurgist in charge of the test, 'to make present-day high-quality steel that brittle, I'd have to lower its temperature to minus 60 or minus 70 degrees Celsius'.

Had the hull been made of steel with a lower sulphur content, it would have bent and stretched, rivets would have popped out and water would have poured in – but at the first impact, the ship would have absorbed massive amounts of the impact energy. It would have slowed, perhaps have bounced away from the iceberg. The sinking would not have come as quickly.

There are more what-ifs. Says Alan Ruffman:

'*If the seamen had known about ice, when they got this cold feeling they might have known to slow down. In thick fog, for example, in the Second World War, my father's ship did not have the radar on. Suddenly it got very chilly. They slowed right down and an iceberg loomed out at them.*

'*The other thing that you can do is to watch for waves breaking at the base of an iceberg: those waves will sometimes activate phosphorescence, a bit of a green sheen around the base. But the night of April 14–15 the seamen at the enquiry said "it was the calmest they had ever seen" – perfect for launching lifeboats but the worst for spotting icebergs. No moon and no waves.*'

'Their' iceberg must have been 90–100 feet high to have dumped ice as it did on the upper decks. It would have easily weighed one million to two million tons and had a draught of between 600 and 800 feet. If only the ship had been going slower: there would have been time to turn.

Fighting the Ice

Many things were never the same again after the *Titanic* sank. Ice was treated with far greater respect. Technology might be able to take ships – and later planes – where they would never have gone before, but ice was clearly not to be messed with. Atlantic shipping took ice messages seriously, steered clear, slowed down. They still do. The winter shipping lane was moved further south. Every passenger ship mounted a twenty-four-hour radio watch; there were to be lifeboats for every person on board.

The American and British Governments with eleven other maritime nations including Canada established the International Ice Patrol, which still operates today. If icebergs are spotted floating towards the shipping lanes by aircraft of the US Coast Guard they are rounded up by Coast Guard patrols. The IIP shares data with Ottawa's Canadian Ice Service which sends out both reconnaissance flights and Canadian Coast Guard ice-breakers. In the Antarctic region, a similar process occurs; in faraway Washington, the National Ice Center uses satellites to track icebergs.

The International Ice Patrol sends out ice charts on a daily basis for shipping. The charts may be superseded in a few hours by rain, sun, wind, the arrival of new icebergs or the toppling or fracturing of old, but overall they give a clear picture of where the danger lies currently and is probably moving to next. Coast guards concentrate on the extent and density of local pack ice.

'My worst fear is the ice pack,' says Jorn Kvinge, skipper of an Alaskan crab boat with many years' experience, 'because when it comes down it hits your [crab] pots and it'll scatter them from here to everywhere. It covers the mud – that stops you fishing. You spend your time looking for your gear again. Production goes to a standstill. If the ice pack's coming, I make sure I'm in the retreat.'

Stopping production on a boat valued at millions of dollars and which 'eats money' to keep in fuel, insured and fully crewed, is no joke. The Bering Sea is no joke either – it's a frightful, freezing, stormy place to sail. If it were not for the crab, the tuna and other catches to be had no one would venture there at all.

Jorn Kvinge: 'We get conditions of extreme winds, up to 80 knots, and big seas. There's a lot of current in the Bering Sea. The current working against the sea can make some big waves and winter time, we get the icy conditions on top of that.'

The pack ice may halt production; but the great weight of superstructure icing on the vessel itself can sink it. The ice comes from sea water hitting metal parts – rigging – anything, in fact, that is exposed to bitter air, cooled super-fast by strong winds and freezing, exactly in the way a deep-freeze works.

'When we get down below 26 degrees Fahrenheit, the ice starts building on the boat. The colder it gets, the faster it sticks. When you get down to 5, 10 degrees, it's like glue; every piece of water that hits the boat sticks and freezes on. It makes it top-heavy and it will roll over if you don't clear the ice off. We put a lot of effort into keeping the boat ice-free.'

Jorn Kvinge remembers the worst time vividly: 'The feeling is the butterflies in your stomach when you see the ice-pack coming at you... that time was five degrees F and blowing fifty... we had put all the gear on board. I was worried that we were not going to be able to do it in time, because we were icing down so hard. We had two people chipping ice twenty-four hours a day and it took us three days to put the gear on because we operate so slowly to stop making spray. That was one of the worst three days of my life.' (For more on the rigours of an Alaskan fisherman's life, see page 135.)

Iceberg Alley

It is not only moving shipping that fears the destructive power of ice. The force of an iceberg, most of its unpredictable shape hidden beneath the surface, slamming into a floating oil platform or its steel or concrete legs, could cause a disaster. As the oil platforms cannot easily move, the iceberg has to be captured, destroyed or steered away. Newfoundland has vast undersea oil reserves. To tap them means that drilling platforms and tankers have to cope with iceberg-infested waters. The national Energy Board and four oil companies (Chevron, Husky, Mobil and Petro-Canada), for example,

Reflected in glassy seas, a majestic iceberg looms against the distant Canadian coastline in the area known as Iceberg Alley – where shipping travels at its peril.

funded iceberg-impact experiments, carried out recently by Memorial University's Centre for Cold Ocean Resources Engineering (C-CORE).

The summer work began, and 1995 was a bumper season for bergs in the North Atlantic with almost three times the usual number of 400 making it as far as Newfoundland. There were plenty of icebergs to choose from, to lasso with a super-strong floating hawser, to tow to the 'berg bank' and to attempt to explode on a precise area of cliff on which was fixed a steel instrument panel that could send quantities of data to cliff-top computers. The only difficulty was doing it.

A reporter named Jim Hutchison went along on the tugboat *Sea Alert* to watch.

'It's like a wild beast that doesn't want to be tamed,' yells tugboat captain Scott Kean. Twisting and turning in the swell, a 30,000-tonne iceberg suddenly capsizes in a curtain of spray, throwing off the towline... As our berg grounds on the rocks near Grappling Island, it splits in half with a thunderous clap. 'That piece is a manageable size for a first impact,' declares project manager Greg Crocker, requesting the captain to snare the 1,000-tonne 'bergy bit'... 'We're feeling our way. Iceberg impacts of this magnitude have never been done before.' The 197-tonne, 32-metre Sea Alert takes up the slack on the two ropes looped through a pulley bolted to the cliff, her powerful engines sending the house-sized berg surging for the panel at a steady four knots.

Crack! Four anchors embedded three metres into solid rock explode out of the cliff face as the pulley tears free, hurling metal and rope like missiles into the sea. Waves snatch at the loose berg and shatter it on rocks far from the target area.

'Iceberg one,' says Crocker ruefully, 'scientists zero.'

And You Can Even Drink It...

Extraordinarily, ice can be the stuff that family firms rest upon. The Kean family of Canada, for example, its roots in seal fishing two centuries ago, today hunts ice, including the big game of the ice world, icebergs.

It has hunted icebergs to crush for fish preserving, to tow away for oil companies, to capture for the same companies who wanted to carry out iceberg research and, most recently, for drinking. Pure iceberg water, made from snow that fell before pollution existed, for Canadian Iceberg vodka and – just for its own self – bottled.

Naturally, hunters need guns. To encourage an iceberg to founder, when it will be easier to tow, 'We use rifles with 303 bullets,' says Ed Kean. 'The bullet doesn't really do anything, it's absorbed in the ice, just like nothing, but the sound of the shell sometimes will make them fall. If there is a weak spot, the force of the bullet might help to do it.'

If not, the hunter has other weapons in the armoury. 'Other times, we got to use a chainsaw and cut a three-foot incision into the ice so we can get some choppers down and start to cut it off that way.'

A lone canoeist explores an icefield off Alaska. Note the pristine beauty of hard blue ice in the foreground, contrasted with the chaotic debris trapped in the Sawyer Glacier in the background.

Standing about on an iceberg with a chainsaw is not like logging. The icebergs quite often roll over for one thing, just like elephants looking to crush an enemy. 'They've got their own mind, you can't stop them when they want to go and they are very unpredictable. They will give you certain signs – cracking and crunching – but you've got to have your wits about you. We've lost a couple of fellas overboard but they've always got their safety gear on. It's a bit dangerous.'

So if the bullets disappear without trace and the chainsaw men are tipped off, how about the heavy guns? Literally. 'Back a few years ago they tried to bomb them and fire torpedoes and it just bounced off, didn't affect the ice at all.'

At this point, the military machine might change the style of weaponry. Chemical, perhaps? 'Another scheme was to paint the iceberg black as black absorbs heat and melts the iceberg that way. After a few hours, the half inch of ice that melted off the surface slid off, taking the black paint with it. It was more or less a big joke and a waste of paint,' concedes Ed Kean.

For a firm like this, a bad ice year does not mean what it sounds like to the rest of the world. It means a year with little ice. Good ice years are those like 1994/5 and 1998, plenty of icebergs close to the Newfoundland and Labrador coast, calving all the time into smaller bergs, more easily harvested with a crane.

Such a year, in this upside-down world, would also be good for ice tourists, for ice is beautiful. The whiteness of an iceberg is air trapped within the original snow crystals. Old ice, which has been melted by rain on its surface, then re-frozen, has less air trapped. It appears green or a stunning blue and is even harder than white iceberg ice. The temperature of icebergs has been found to be minus 10 to minus 20 degrees Centigrade, as cold as the original glacier and as hard as rock. Like floating islands, too, they carry their own microclimates with them, sometimes swirling fog, mist and chill, and their own colonies of birds and animals and schools of fish feeding on plankton that cling to the underside.

Ice Islands

After the Second World War, massive islands of floating ice were first discovered in Arctic seas by the United States. Island T-1 (Target-1) was picked up by an Air Force plane's radar in 1946 – a land mass where none were supposed to be. Many of the islands are just great blocks of ice; but a few actually have dark 'hills' composed of rocks. Arlis, an ice island defunct since the late 1960s, was broken off the Ellesmere ice shelf, where boulders and other debris from the land had spilled down with the glacier that fed it. This rock cover in fact insulated Arlis from melting in the heat of the sun as it slowly drifted south, prolonging its life to several years.

Historically, old maps have shown islands which mysteriously ceased to exist, giving rise to extraordinary legends. In 1931 Takpuk Island was discovered, examined and photographed by Eskimos. This was probably an ice island the Americans named Arlis II (Arctic Research Laboratory Ice Station No. 2).

All these islands were enormous: T-3 was 6 miles long and 3 miles wide. Some of them are manned by scientists for years on end – T-3 has been manned from March 1952, as a kind of US forward warning station during the entire Cold War with the USSR, as well as a scientific research platform.

Bernt Balchen, Arctic explorer and the first man to pilot a plane over both poles, explains the importance of manning these ice islands that are occupied on a first come first served basis. He wrote in his book, *Come North With Me*: 'In Roman times the Mediterranean Sea was considered the centre of the world, but our new Mediterranean is the Arctic Ocean and the North Pole is the cross-roads of tomorrow's travel.'

The Americans have discussed using these ephemeral islands as nuclear submarine stations – and even, some time in the future, as depots for undersea nuclear-powered commerce, a place where undersea freighters and tankers could hook up. This is interesting, but dangerous. Apart from the pollution generated which destroys our environment and aids global warming, these ice islands are not permanent – they are not even very stable. Arlis II was manned for just four years until it turned maverick and escaped the Arctic Ocean to journey southward and fragment into dozens of smaller – and very dangerous – icebergs, as it melted in crowded sea-lanes.

The Most Savage Sea of All

It is in Antarctica that the greatest beauty of ice is to be found. Nowhere else on Earth are there sights to equal its vast icebergs and ice shelves, just as Antarctica earns all the other superlatives: the most isolated and remote continent, the hardest to reach, the last discovered, the driest, the windiest, the highest, the coldest, the least populated; all set within perhaps the most savage sea of all, the Southern Ocean.

Beautiful but, of course, deadly. The cold of the region can quickly kill the unprotected and even the protected can be rendered helpless by blizzards, a frequent occurrence. Very little, if any, snow falls during one of these storms. Snow is simply picked up by the ferocious wind and blown across the surface, causing blinding conditions in which objects less than a yard away may become indistinguishable.

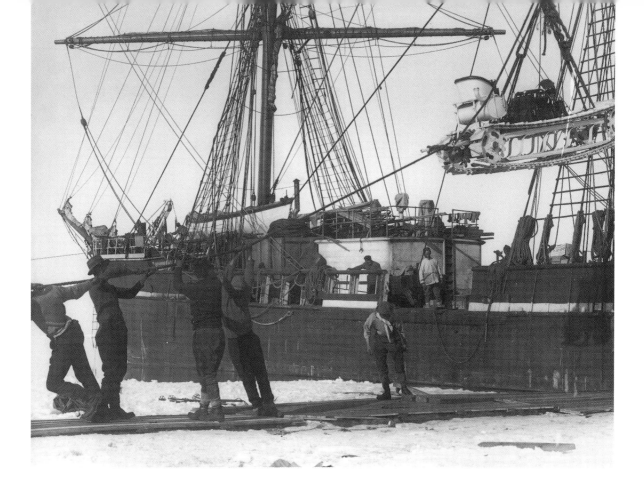

Getting the cumbersome, motor-sledges off the *Terra Nova* during Scott's ill-fated 1911–12 expedition to the South Pole.

Several people have died just inches from safety because they could not find their way back to base.

Lawrence Oates, of 'I am just going outside and may be some time' fame, is credited with having done this deliberately because he could stand the wait for death no longer on the *Terra Nova* Expedition of 1911–12 led by Captain Robert Falcon Scott. It is somehow an eerie realization that, just two weeks after Scott's last diary entry on 29 March 1912 – and his death from cold and slow starvation either that day or soon after – the cold of a sea at the opposite end of the globe killed 1,513 pioneers of a different sort. The memory of Scott's crazy amateurism but heroic endurance and the fate of those who had faith that they were in a ship that nothing could sink have lasted to this day, awful warnings of the necessity not to trifle with the polar regions of the globe.

The *Terra Nova* Expedition nearly came to an end before it started, in December 1910. Three days after sailing from New Zealand into the Southern Ocean, the ship was hit by a 36-hour screaming gale so typical of the region. It nearly sank the ship, an old Scottish whaler. Perhaps Scott should have taken it as a premonition. Roald Amundsen sailed from Norway in June 1911 in *Fram* – the same specially strengthened ship in which Nansen had demonstrated polar drift – which possessed a diesel engine rather than a coal-fired steam one and so started faster, as well as a rounded hull which could rise up out of pressing ice floes. En route, he tossed off the infamous telegram to Scott: 'Beg leave to inform you *Fram* proceeding Antarctic.' The rest is history (and *Fram* can still be seen, a national monument in its own museum near Oslo) but no matter how current the exploration – or mad the journey as some see it – disaster can still strike.

In 1986, for example, Robert Swan, Roger Mear and Gareth Wood walked Scott's route to the South Pole, man-hauling sledges, 883 miles in seventy days. Like Scott, they got there. Like Scott, they promptly had bad news: that their 550-ton trawler, supply ship and floating home, *Southern Quest*, had been crushed by the worst pack ice seen in thirty years off Beaufort Island. A simultaneous fire in the engine room meant instant evacuation of crew, equipment and provisions on to the ice, from where the crew watched the ship sink in minutes.

As Swan remembers bitterly (and accurately), receiving the news 'jerked me savagely back into the real world, for the sinking of the *Southern Quest* would play into the hands of those who wanted to prohibit private expeditions from Antarctica, an issue that had been hotly debated for some time. The expedition would now be portrayed as foolhardy and dangerous, implying (quite wrongly) that ultimately we were dependent on government intervention and generosity.'

The expedition's aircraft, a modified Cessna 185 flown by Giles Kershaw, a legend in polar flight, was on standby near Ross Island to retrieve the trio from the Pole. US helicopters, however, picked up the ship's crew and took them to McMurdo. There was a bizarre stand-off: Kershaw had to agree not to fly to the Pole in exchange for the US not calling the collection and flying of *Southern Quest*'s crew to New Zealand a 'rescue' (the expedition was charged US$80,000 for the flights). It brought relations between governments and private expeditions to an all-time low. After almost innumerable daring flights over Antarctic seas and land, Giles Kershaw was eventually killed in a gyrocopter crash on the Antarctic Peninsula in March 1990.

But while lone sailors and determined explorers still seek to-the-edge experiences in Antarctic seas, perfectly ordinary people also brave the Southern Ocean as tourists aboard cruise ships. They are travelling for the scenery and the wildlife, both of which are spectacular, in the Antarctic summer, when clothes suitable for a tough Northern Hemisphere winter will suffice. The cruise ships are on the spartan side and will still demand vigilance: vessels pushing through ice can lurch and bump suddenly and passengers are told to always 'keep one hand for the ship' so they can grab something to steady themselves. Top bunks come with straps and expensive camera equipment is best kept on the floor so it can't fall anywhere. Lifeboat drill is taken very seriously, for 'stormy' and 'Southern Ocean' are simply synonymous.

The Southern Ocean, as well as connecting the Atlantic, Pacific and Indian Oceans in a continuous ring of mainly eastward flowing water, insulates Antarctica from warm water. The Antarctic Circumpolar Current has an average rate of flow four times that of the Gulf Stream. It's fast and strong, in particular, through the narrow strait of Drake Passage, between the tip of South America and the Antarctic Peninsula. It is here that deep, dangerous low pressure systems funnel while the occasional sailor waits for a gap.

As ice shelves melt just south of the Polar Front – where Antarctic water meets the warmer water of the north – the coldest, densest sea water in the world sinks to the bottom of the ocean. It travels north along the ocean floor, affecting the surface by reducing the temperature of the seas and adding oxygen, released from melted ice, to them. This cooling effect on the oceans is an important part of the heat balance of the world and is the subject of much scientific research.

There are other, more local, currents circulating: such as the East Wind Drift which mixes with the water leaving the Weddell Sea and flows north to mix again with the circumpolar current in the Scotia Sea. Another powerful source of temperature control are the massive freshwater (from melted ice) convection cells around the ice shelf. The combination of all these currents and water mixings is part of what makes the fearful weather of the region – fearful but vital, for the cooling effects of the currents are transmitted to the rest of the globe and are part of what makes the Earth inhabitable.

It is known that the world sea level has risen about 10 centimetres in the past 100 years and is increasing by about one or two millimetres each year. Three key factors that would contribute to a further increase are: expansion of the volume of the world's oceans as they warm up; melting of valley glaciers; faster melting of the ice sheets of Greenland and Antarctica. In the past 100 years it seems as though the Antarctica ice sheet has stayed roughly stable, which is just as well. It would take only a minor melting of this ice to produce the most insidiously savage sea of all: one that gradually drowns inhabited coastal regions. Alarmingly, there are beginning to be signs that this may be starting to happen.

It is from Antarctica, of course, that the iceberg record-breakers come. B-9, calved in 1987, was 154 kilometres long and 35 kilometres wide, roughly the size of Prince Edward Island. Scientists estimated that it would take up to twenty years to melt. The biggest ever came in 1956, 330 kilometres long and 96 wide. This was in the period of mindless military tests which found that it took more than 2,000 tons of TNT to melt an average sized iceberg.

In 1986, A22B, a lump the size of Northern Ireland, broke from the Filchner Ice Shelf, taking three research bases and colonies of penguins and albatrosses with it. It split into three pieces soon afterwards, grounded in the frozen, shallow waters of the Weddell Sea. In 1991 one of the pieces, A22A, freed itself and headed for the Falkland Islands, eventually breaking up in storms off them. Seven years later, its big sister, A22B, 35 miles long and 12 miles wide, set off at the stately pace of a mile a day towards either Brazil or South Africa, depending on currents. As it melted, its pace quickened. The immediate danger it may pose is that as it melts, a trail of smaller fragments are left behind in waters that have never seen an iceberg, traps for startled mariners.

The real danger is that it may be an indicator of increasing break-up of the southern ice-cap. Five ice shelves have collapsed over the past fifty years. The most recent were Larsen A and B. Scientists are divided over whether this is to do with global warming, for only parts of Antarctica seem to be getting warmer. Subtle changes in ocean currents could be responsible.

But that begs the question: What is causing the subtle changes? For the only thing known with certainty about the long-term effects of global warming on the Earth's seas is that they are hard to predict. Twisting the kaleidoscope of currents will produce a new picture and we may or may not be in it.

COLD WATER SHOCK

Humans cannot tolerate extremes of temperature. Intense heat and intense cold destroy our bodies and most people hope never to encounter the extremes. In practice, we are all too often inches from them – cooking over hot flames or driving through a winter night – but unprepared for disaster.

Take the 2,224 passengers and crew on the *Titanic* on the evening of 14 April 1912; or four friends playing cards on the *Cougar*, a small fishing boat they had hired one September; or the cross-section of people travelling to Sweden from Estonia on the ferry that bore the latter country's name. None imagined that in a few hours they would be fighting for their survival in the icy waters from which they seemed so insulated. If commerce and technology have combined to produce a reassuring environment, whether a luxury liner with carpets and an orchestra or a working boat with a table, cards and a bottle of beer, then people are lulled into a sense of security. The professionals are doing their job, they think, leave it to them. Safety drill is a murmur in the background.

Yet a few passengers will at some point stare over the rail, down into the deep water, at waves that are green and sparkling or grey and turbulent and will wonder: What would happen if I fell in? What should I do? Am I a strong enough swimmer?

The sea has many ways to kill. The chief one is simply its coldness. This was probably understood as far back as 450 BC when the Greek historian Herodotus described an ill-fated sea-going campaign, distinguishing between those who died because they could not swim and those who died from cold.

The distinction, however, was forgotten. Despite the clues given again and again by those who helplessly watched people die, the role of temperature, as opposed to

View from a helicopter: often a helicopter is the quickest means possible of rescue at sea – and, when people are overboard in icy water, minutes count.

drowning, was not really grasped until the Second World War when two-thirds of the approximately 45,000 who died while serving with the British Royal Navy did so not from wounds or drowning following enemy action but from hypothermia and exposure because of immersion – being completely dipped – in cold water.

Dr Mike Tipton is both Reader at the University of Portsmouth and Head of Environmental Medicine at the Institute of Naval Medicine, Alverstoke, Hampshire, a leading research facility in naval and diving medicine. He says, 'The death certificates of those who died from the *Titanic* said they died from drowning. But the sea was calm and those in the water probably had flotation equipment with them because there were a significant number of lifebelts available. Many in fact did drown once hypothermia had set in, but it wasn't because they couldn't stay afloat. They died because the sea was icy cold; but the lesson of cold was missed. Surviving in the sea isn't just a case of staying afloat but *warm* and afloat.'

May 1940: survivors from a torpedoed French warship are picked up. It was not realized until 50 years later that lifting hypothermic survivors vertically out of icy water often killed them as warm blood flowed away from the body's core.

There are four stages of physical reaction to cold water immersion (see box opposite). It is a hideous irony that the fourth phase – the rescue attempt – can in fact contribute to so many deaths in itself (as the box explains). The phenomenon has only recently been recognized, following research by Admiral Frank Golden at the Institute of Naval Medicine.

There is a curious historical footnote here. Before Admiral Golden's work, the accepted wisdom was that, on rescue, warmer blood from the body's core began to return to surface skin. As that skin was still frozen, the blood bravely travelling there became refrigerated, causing what was termed the 'afterdrop' in temperature that could cause death. That 'wisdom' has been gained from experiments on human subjects done by the Nazis at Dachau concentration camp. Yet, at the same time that those gruesome experiments were being carried out, the German Air Sea Rescue services, picking up both Luftwaffe and Royal Air Force survivors, were discovering that those they lifted out of freezing seas horizontally on ladders survived better than the ones picked up vertically.

How cold does cold water have to be to have these effects? From 15 degrees Celsius downwards is the danger zone and that covers most of the world's sea waters. The waters around the British Isles, for example, vary from about 5 to 15 degrees Celsius; the average sea bottom temperature all around the world is 4 degrees C.

Because the human body at rest continuously produces energy in the form of heat at the rate of 80 watts – a bit more than an average light bulb – 'thermal neutral' is air or water

Cold water immersion

There are four stages of physical reaction to cold water immersion, any one of which can lead to death.

Phase 1 Cold shock response

The vast proportion of open water deaths occur during the first three minutes. The shock of plunging into icy water causes a physical panic reaction manifested by a terrible gasping and chronic inability to hold the breath.

Phase 2 Short-term immersion

The next stage is up until half an hour in the water. The whole body begins to cool quickly, from the outside to the centre. The first areas to cool are limbs and muscles in fingers, hands, forearms and feet which significantly reduces the ability to swim, climb aboard a liferaft or open distress flares.

Phase 3 Long-term immersion

This is the phase from 30 minutes until rescue – if it comes. The body cools to levels which cause hypothermia, the cooling not just of skin and muscle but of the heart and brain, which in turn causes disorientation, confusion and amnesia. The victim drifts into semi-consciousness. Once the body temperature drops to 30–33 degrees Celsius, with no lifejacket the victim will probably be unable to stay conscious long enough to keep head above water and so will drown. The extreme temperature below which the heart muscle can't function is 25 degrees Celsius. Before death the victim will appear dead, profoundly cold, with no discernible heart-beat or pulse.

Phase 4 Rescue collapse

About 17 per cent of immersion deaths occur at the moment of rescue. Pulling people out of the water in a vertical position is a final challenge to their heart and brain: the effects of gravity mean that the remaining blood supply to these organs is drained away suddenly. Paradoxically, the hydrostatic squeeze of seawater actually helps keep blood circulating round the body; suddenly plucking the body out of that hydrostatic squeeze may precipitate the terminal heart attack. The solution is to lift people out horizontally but this is not always possible in emergency rescues.

temperature about 2 degrees below normal body temperature of 37 degrees C, to take account of the fact that the body does put out the equivalent of 2 degrees C of heat. Between 35 degrees C down to 25 degrees C, the body can continue to exercise and so generate heat and maintain a reasonable body temperature until exhausted – which could be quite a while, depending on the fitness, health and age of the person in the water.

Below 25 degrees C, the cold shock response can potentially be suppressed and the victim can cope for a while. Even if they cannot voluntarily exercise, uncontrollable shivering produces some exercise warmth. But below 15 degrees C, the cold shock reaction is uncontrollable.

The Night the *Estonia* Ferry Sank

Of course, whatever temperature the sea is at, it is not always calm and still enough for the victims of accidents to bob about like corks, hoping to be rescued before they slowly freeze to death. On the night of 27–28 September 1994, it was not especially calm in the Baltic Sea.

The Baltic is an inland sea lying north of a coastline that takes in Germany, Poland, a scrap of Russia and the Lit, Lat and Est of the Baltic States (Lithuania, Latvia and

Estonia). It reaches to Finland and Sweden but its only connection with the seas beyond is through three narrow channels between Sweden and the Danish islands: the Sound, the Great Belt and the Little Belt. For this reason and because of the many rivers which drain into it, the Baltic is fresher than normal sea water and, because it is cut off from the warm Gulf Stream, large areas are frozen over each winter. It is a cold, 'thin' sea, harder to stay afloat in than saltier seas.

That night, a southwest wind blew across the Baltic, all the way from England, a long 'fetch' from which high waves developed. It was a strong wind – 30 knots and stronger in the gusts – which produced, for the Baltic, a high to very high 'sea state' of waves about 6–10 metres from trough to crest. It was also cold and raining.

When the ship left port that evening, though, it seemed simply windy. The skies were clear and the sea, protected by an island, seemed reasonably calm. People ate dinner and enjoyed some entertainment in the lounge areas or went unworried to their cabins; though Mikael Oun, a Swedish aid worker, had noticed that waves in the ferry's swimming pool were hitting the ceiling. They were not to know that the bow entry hull doors were not properly closed and would shortly open wide, letting the sea rush in.

Towards midnight, the weather worsened and the waves built up. Across the ship, people were woken suddenly from sleep by a loud bang – 'like a metal to metal noise', remembers Pierre Thiger, a Swedish marine designer who was still up and in the bar. 'My first thought was that we had crashed into another ship or a submarine... it was a very distinct sound.' Two more bangs followed – the bow doors crashing back and forth before they were ripped away – and the ship stopped rolling and began to tilt and rock backwards and forwards before being flung to one side at an angle of 35 degrees which rapidly became 40 and 45 degrees.

Pierre Thiger recalls: 'When the big list came... the furniture and everything... people... were just thrown through the air. I started my way up towards the exit... people were climbing on top of each other... there was not much screaming but a few were crying.'

For Sara Hedrenius, who was returning from Estonia after visiting her father, the capsizing was like a bad dream. She had been asleep in one of the lounges on a sofa when a 'loud bang' disturbed her, but she continued in a half sleep. She came fully awake when the ship started to tip up so fast she fell. Her first thoughts were that she might drown and she grabbed her passport so her body would be identified. People were so shocked they couldn't speak. Almost in a dream-like state, they made eye contact, waiting for something to happen. Everything was upside down. 'I saw a man who got an ashtray on his head and he fell down, bleeding,' Sara says.

Maria Fägersten, who had been at a police conference with sixty-seven others, was dancing in the karaoke bar when the ferry started to list within twenty-five minutes of the first bang. 'The whole kitchen came over me,' she remembers, describing how the walls and equipment of the kitchen area seemed to fly through the air on to the dance floor. As the ship slipped sideways many people just seemed to disappear. Maria made her way out to a deck. 'I saw people in a state of shock. They were crying, screaming... then a few of them just jumped over the ship and I couldn't understand why because the water was too cold and dark. The sea was awful – waves between 8 and 12 metres high.'

Tom Johnson, a Stockholm policeman who had also been at the conference, said that he and his friends had been joking about the *Titanic* earlier that evening. Feeling seasick, he went to his cabin and tried to sleep. When he heard the bang, he got up and started to dress, but by the time he had pulled on a shirt and some underwear, the ship was listing badly and he decided to get out quickly. 'In the corridor, people were crashing into the wall, into the doors, on the starboard side. The port side was up on heaven... floors had become walls.'

There were more than 1,000 crew and passengers aboard. With the ship at a 45-degree angle on its side, most of them tried, in various states of dress, to get up to higher decks or to the outside of the ship. Some found lifejackets or lifebelts, many did not. Anders Ericson, who had been sleeping in a fourth-deck cabin, was woken by the first bang, reacted quickly, put on trousers and a shirt and got up to the seventh deck with a bit of a climb, from where he helped others climb up and gave out lifejackets. He then scrambled up to a position behind the main bridge, just below the lifeboat station.

Paul Barney, a British landscape architect returning from an ecological development conference in Estonia, had been asleep in the cafe. When he woke, the ferry was almost on its side and he was cut by the glass and plates flying around. He put on a jumper and decided to leave his boots in case he had to swim. He used his trained 'mind's eye' to transform the tipped deck into a landscape and headed upwards as if he were crossing rough terrain, not thinking about anything apart from how to get out and his determination not to die.

Pierre Thiger also had only one thought: to get out. He somehow managed to climb up the walls, using lights and wall fittings as grips, and got on to the promenade deck. There was no sign of the crew but passengers were throwing the lifebelts to each other. He put on one and climbed over the railing as waves of 15 to 20 metres were climbing up the ship and shooting into the night sky like rockets. People were flung out each time one hit them.

Pierre clung on to the side of the ship, his feet jammed for security into air vents, while he tried to decide whether to jump into the huge sea. 'It was very windy, it was raining and completely dark... the clouds were passing by at very

Salvage crews raise the 56-ton bow door which was ripped off the *Estonia* ferry, causing it to sink in less than thirty minutes in the Baltic Sea off Finland one dark and stormy night in September 1994. It was cold water that killed many of the 852 victims while they waited to be rescued.

high speed and the moonshine went through at short periods so it almost looked like flashes... you saw people in different motions... it was a spectacular scenario... very unreal... I thought, just a few minutes back, we were sitting on the inside and music was playing – and all of a sudden, this.'

Pierre was one of about 100 people clinging on to the outside of the ship: most passengers opted to remain inside. Many of those on the outside were climbing for the highest place but Pierre suddenly realized that he might well end up 100 metres above the sea if the bow went up vertically when the stern went down. 'It was almost like rats,' he says, 'on a ship everybody clings to the top position... so I stopped in the middle. I was not prepared when a wave came up with enormous force and ripped me out of my location – like somebody throwing a tub of water into your face... I was travelling upwards... like a rollercoaster... down down down with enormous speed... I saw many people lose their grips and fall down into the cranes and boats... so my only thought was to cover my head with my hands and I just waited for the big bang.'

There was no bang – in fact, there was no sound. Pierre had gone so deep under water he felt his lungs about to explode with the pressure. When he came up, he saw the ship going down vertically. He felt alone, but saw a liferaft about 200 metres away. Although feeling weak and cold he realized it was his only chance. It was also a chance possibly only he could take for Pierre had been a professional swimmer in his youth. He swam against the huge waves, losing sense of direction. Somehow he made it, but had no strength to drag himself aboard. The rope around the raft was tangled and too high for him to reach but he mustered enough strength to raise a leg and push his big toe into the twisted rope. Then he forced himself out of the water and on to the raft.

His problems were far from over as the roof of the raft had caved in under the pressure of water and he was tossed about in it 'like a pot boiling'. For the next few hours, Pierre, alone on the raft, was first in a fit of fury about its bad design and then occupied himself by mentally designing a new one.

Meanwhile, Paul had jumped into the sea towards a raft which some people were inflating. A wave tipped it upside-down and he had to swim under it and then haul himself back on with waves crashing down. Sixteen people drifted away from the sinking ship, freezing cold. Being in a dangerous situation was not a new experience for Paul, whose independent, rugged lifestyle had included trekking in the Himalayas – but he was angry, incensed, in fact, with the possibility that he might die. 'I hadn't finished with my life... there had to be something else I could do to save my life... I knew if I entered into semi-unconsciousness which is the overwhelming desire you get with hypothermia, to put your head down and fall asleep... and my God, the sight of that liferaft felt so cosy... it seemed better to be asleep because it was an escape... people who were dead seemed in a much nicer place... I was probably so cold and almost dead... but I chose to stay alive.'

However, around Paul on the raft, people began to die: an Estonian girl slid off when it overturned. 'When you've seen a few go, you know the signs. They throw themselves around and groan a lot and grab on to you. They were either washed overboard or froze to death.' By dawn there were only eight still alive.

Anders Ericson was also thrown from the *Estonia*, towards a raft that turned out to be capsized. Somehow he crawled into its tent section, under water, but managed to keep afloat and with his top half out of the water because of his lifejacket and his success at hanging on to ropes inside the raft. Air came in when the raft tossed up. 'As long as I felt alive and could feel my hands I decided that I was going to come home again.'

The first rescue helicopter on the scene that night was from Turku Search and Rescue in Finland which arrived at about 3 am. The helicopter team found no one alive in the water or in the first three rafts their winchman visited. Eventually, with the help of an extra winchman (conditions were so poor that the winchmen had to rest between missions) they picked up forty-four survivors. Helicopter winchman and diver Johan Steene, bobbing up and down on the end of the winch wire like – as Pierre Thiger described it – 'a teabag being dunked in a teapot', describes what he found: 'On this raft I saw three men, one almost naked with his underwear on and two other men with a little bit of clothes... the undressed man was really in a bad shape, really cold, almost unconscious.'

Anders Ericson, Pierre Thiger and Paul Barney were rescued between 4 and 6 am. Once transferred to a Finnish ship by exhausted winchman Johan Steene – who says, 'I never thought I would work in waves 7–10 metres high' – Pierre, the first aboard, describes how his whole body buckled and he collapsed on the floor, his strength gone.

The *Estonia* sinking has all the elements of terror: dark, cold, gales, huge waves, the unexpected midnight sinking and the awful loss of 852 lives. Anders, Pierre and Paul were among the relatively few rescued.

It is also frightening because it seemed that only fit, young, psychologically prepared, strong individuals survived; the 'ordinary' perished. The sinking ship was so difficult to traverse and the sea so fierce as well as cold that those who did make the decision to leave the ship needed to have plenty of physical strength to do so and subsequently to be able to climb into a liferaft as well as enough mental strength to keep themselves alert.

In dramatic situations, strength will help. Experiments at the Institute of Naval Medicine have shown that fitness and the ability to swim well can help cope with the initial cold water shock responses. Apart from anything else, swimmers are used to being tipped into water and people can be trained to at least brace themselves for cold water shock. However, fitness may help people continue to produce a little heat but 'goes nowhere near providing full protection', explains Dr Mike Tipton. 'Even international class swimmers will very quickly be incapacitated on immersion in very cold water. Fitness tends to be associated with low levels of body fat.'

So, strangely, the dispassionate sea can claim the athlete but spare the physically weaker but fatter person. Fat beneath human skin acts like insulation from the cold, slowing the deadly cooling of the body's inner core of heart and brain. Surviving exposure after the first cold shock phase often favours the plumper (because of their body shape, this includes women) over the fitter but leaner person. It's not for nothing that long-distance swimmers who are tackling chilly seas such as the English Channel deliberately eat to gain fat before they swim.

What's more, trying to keep swimming to generate heat to keep the body warm in very cold water is actually nonsense physiology. Swimming uses leg and arm muscles and the muscles demand blood to bring them sugars and oxygen. That blood will be transferred away from the 'core' of heart and lungs where it is actually doing more good. The legs and arms effectively are radiators with a high surface area out of which heat can quickly be lost. Swimming also stirs up water around the body, thus increasing cooling.

The only virtue in swimming is if a short time of it will bring you to a place of greater safety out of the water as – again despite misconceptions gained from heated swimming pools – air is warmer than cold sea water. Water transfers heat away from the body twenty-five times faster than air of the same temperature. The liferaft or boat is a godsend but even so, they could be termed 'the life-if-you're-lucky rafts'. *Have they been properly maintained, do they work, do they have a hood, have they landed the right way up?*

Be Prepared...

In some cases, do they even exist? Take the case of the *Cougar*, a small boat hired for a day of fishing and fun. Even the most relaxed summer's day outing can turn into a cold-water nightmare when least expected. In September 1988 the *Cougar* was chartered in Oregon by a group of friends for a day of tuna fishing. What none of them knew was that the *Cougar*'s skipper had never been on a deep sea trip before; the boat usually fished only a few kilometres from the coast. The boat carried only its usual limited safety gear and an inshore radio. What it didn't carry was a working bilge pump: it was faulty but Captain Pat Watson had hoped that it would hold out. Vessels licensed to carry fewer than six passengers have no mandatory safety inspections in this part of the world – as is the case in many places elsewhere.

The boat was 80 kilometres out to sea when the inevitable happened: the bilge pump broke down totally. Two hours later, the boat had sunk and the passengers were in the icy sea.

They knew that it was essential to keep warm. Even wet clothes to act as a barrier against the water conducting heat away from the body were better than too few clothes. But, between them, there weren't that many clothes. The *Cougar* may have been small but if it had possessed an inflatable raft, three people might not have met such a terrible end. Might not – but after cold water immersion, nothing is guaranteed. Someone who has fallen in the sea, survived the cold shock response, cooled down considerably and has no change of clothes but is helped on to a liferaft is in a better position but by no means assured of survival. Only warming will assure survival.

It is on this principle that the remarkable item called the survival or abandonment suit is constructed. There is a lot of confusion about the correct terminology for these garments. Briefly, the 'wet suit' is what people in water having fun wear. It gives the short-term ability to stay in the water longer. A 'dry suit' with no insulation is what, for example, North Sea pilots wear on top of ordinary clothing. A dry suit, with its own insulation, waterproof, with watertight neck and face seals made of Neoprene, integral feet and attached mitts that can be worn once the hands have been used for manipulating window catches or flares or whatever else necessary, is the king of survival suits. The problem with it is that you cannot wear it – or, to some extent, even those without insulation – while you are working: you become far too hot as their entire *raison d'être* is not to let heat escape from the body. Yet these suits mean the difference between life and death for anyone running risks in cold water.

The icy and forbidding waters of the Bering Sea.

Alaskan Crab Roulette

For the men who risk their lives fishing in some of the most hazardous waters the world has to offer on both the furthermost sides of North America in the Bering Sea, which crams its icy bulk between Alaska and Siberia, and in the North Atlantic, the survival suit is as much an everyday item as a lunchtime sandwich or a newspaper is to those who work in the padded tranquillity of an office.

These men are cowboys on a salt-air frontier who do not fish in the conventional sense of the word. To start with – deaths are a part of the dues. 'Oh, we expect to lose one a month,' locals say casually. In fact, the death rate is far higher even than that. In 1997 in Kodiak alone, nineteen men and women were lost at sea in the mad scramble for King Crab, working for an industry whose rapaciousness has to be held in check by government in order that it does not destroy its own livelihood by overfishing. They service ships that are often travelling factories, but ones that demand that death is faced daily in order to service the onboard freezers, slicers and pulpers.

Above Kodiak, Alaska, home to one of the fiercely competitive fishing fleets. The battle for the 6-foot crabs found in the Bering Sea causes 100 times more deaths than any other industry in the United States.

Right Fishermen in the Bering Sea aboard a crab boat, struggling in the bitter cold to empty a huge metal cage or 'pot'. In such conditions, accidents are frequent.

And the times of the year when the weather is at its worst are when the crabs and scallops found in cold Arctic seas are at their best. Where the 6-foot king crabs are concerned, overfishing by big American ships has reduced the shellfish populations; to collect the limited quotas now allowed, the ships dash out of port and fight with each other and the weather in a mad, sleepless frenzy that will scrape off the ocean floor in a few days what once took all year when the industry was locally based.

If you're looking for the toughest, most intensive fishing conducted in freezing temperatures and often mountainous seas, crab fishing in the Alaskan Aleutian Islands is it. Low pressure areas march across from Siberia, reacting with high pressure over Alaska to create monstrous weather. Most search and rescue cases in Alaska are weather-related.

There is always respect and a creeping fear during major storms out in the Bering Sea. The sea can be so rough and hazardous that in 1998, at the start of the four-day Alaskan king crab season, the US Coast Guard – responding to past disasters – for the first time despatched rescue ships out to the Aleutians in *anticipation* of the inevitable.

According to Arnie Thomson from the Alaska Crab Coalition, the boats often experience 50 mph winds and waves between 20 and 30 feet. A common statement among the crews at the end of an average day is, 'Boy, the weather was really savage today!'

But why are so many fishermen desperate to get on one of the 250 crab boats for such a short season? The king crab season begins on 1 November and lasts for just four days. The next major crab season starts on 15 January, when, for four to eight weeks (depending on how long it takes them to achieve the quota), boats will be chasing £225 million worth of the opilio crab. All the boats compete to fish the largest quota in what is called the 'Olympic' system – he who wins the race, wins the prize.

Individual boats can make between $800,000 and $1 million in two short seasons, so it's hardly surprising that fishermen travel for hundreds of miles to get a position on a crab boat. The boats are moored at Kodiak Island or Dutch Harbour – but the fishermen come from Oregon, Washington State and from across Alaska.

Even the boats themselves are dangerous; 125 feet long, with tiny and basic crew quarters, while on deck there is highly dangerous machinery – cranes and winches for throwing the huge (750-pound) metal crab 'pots' or cages overboard to sit 500 to 1,000 feet below on the sea bed and heaving them back in, hopefully full of the giant crabs that aggregate in these shallow polar waters. The men work at incredible pace, eating on the hoof and snatching sleep here and there.

The *Seattle Times and Post-Intelligencer* describes it:

This week about 235 fishing boats, most from the Puget Sound region, will converge on the Bering Sea for the opilio crab season. The annual event has come to approximate the Alaskan gold rush, a convergence of opportunism, horrible weather and a life-threatening race against the clock... The winter crabbing season seems almost diabolically designed for

A port in the Aleutian Islands in the Bering Straits, where many fishing boats unload their catch or seek shelter from forming ice.

accident, injury and death. When the air is colder than the water, boats heavily laden with crab pots can ice up, destabilize and sink within minutes... Manned with sledge hammers, the crew chips away at the ice, sometimes for days. Skippers can go for five days without sleep . . .

But if the catch is good, the financial rewards are, for a brief time, exhilarating. It is an Arctic roulette and, in the crab fishery, accidental death is nearly 100 times the national American average. As in roulette, there is a price to be paid.

Men Overboard!

On 15 March 1990, one month into the season, the crab boat, the *Alaskan Monarch*, got into difficulties in ice off the Pribilof Islands, some way north of the Aleutians in the Bering Sea – literally, in the middle of nowhere. Its holds filled to the brim with crab, the *Monarch* was steaming into the harbour of St Paul's, one of the Pribilofs, to off-load its catch at a processing plant there. As it approached the harbour, there was a build-up of ice; then the wind direction changed and the vessel became stuck in the ice.

Skipper Morris Hanson alerted the Alaskan Coast Guard, asking for assistance, even though he wasn't immediately too worried since the sea was calm and they were in shallow water.

Alan Doty, now retired after twenty-six years with the Coast Guard, was on patrol at Lost Harbour 300 miles away on the far side of the Aleutians in the cutter *Storis* when the call came in. 'We blasted out of there because it would take 18 hours to reach the *Monarch*... when we approached the vessel the following morning, there was a raft of ice inroaded against the western shore of the island. As we got closer, we prepared to launch a tow line but the skipper then reported that the ice was moving the vessel slowly towards the shore and a line of rocks. We were running out of time.'

The cutter moved into the ice but could make only slow progress. They tried to pass the *Monarch* a line but the crab boat was slowly moving out of reach.

Meanwhile, a helicopter had been scrambled from Kodiak Island, four hours away, to help in the rescue. Pilot Laura Guth says: 'At that stage... there was no real urgency at all. The weather had been okay up to that point, but the Bering Sea was starting to look nasty. We heard someone on the stricken vessel say they were going to put on their survival suits as they were heading towards the rocks. Once we heard this, we stepped things up a gear and realized that the boat was in real trouble.'

The winds were blowing at 30 knots and visibility was down to one and a half miles when Laura received a message from Skipper Hanson, asking if they could hoist one of the crew members off the boat since his survival suit had fallen over the side. If the man went into the ice-cold sea without his suit, he would survive for just two minutes.

Laura Guth: 'We started to hover over the vehicle. At first we thought we could hoist from the mid-deck, but it was covered in ice and inaccessible, so we decided to start hoisting from the bow. I instructed the skipper to send one man across to the bow... but four rushed across together! We got the four crew members off... the helicopter was creating a lot of downwash so we had to move away and leave the skipper and the chief engineer still on board.'

The Coast Guard cutter tried one last time to get a line across – and then the *Monarch* was on the rocks. The boat tilted as Skipper Hanson and the engineer made their way across the deck to evacuate. Hanson describes what happened next: 'I slipped as a down-wave caught us. I was slammed against the rail and then washed over the side. We were both wearing survival suits so our main concern then was that the vessel would crush us both. The boat seemed to go one way and we went the other. I ended up against a wall of ice, with a block of ice on top of me. I remember the wind being particularly fierce. It must have been blowing at about 40 knots.'

Coast Guard Doty describes it: 'I really thought we had lost them at that point. They were in serious trouble. It was a gut wrencher. You're all working to try to get the people off... then this wave comes along and carries the final two overboard.'

Despite the ice, there was a large ocean swell of about 15 feet running in the area that day. Waves typically break as the water becomes shallow – and the boat had

US Coast Guard helicopter pilot, Lieutenant Commander Laura Guth has rescued many Alaskan ships in difficulty in the freezing Bering Sea. One of her missions was to rescue the crew of the *Alaskan Monarch*, a crab boat trapped in ice.

grounded on rocks in very shallow water, hence the fateful wave that seemed to rear up out of nowhere through the blocks of floating ice.

Laura was watching while she hovered close to the vessel:

'As the skipper walked across the mid-deck he slipped, just as a huge wave seemed to come from nowhere and went over the top… scattering the skipper and the chief engineer, who both went over the side. The waves were coming in sets. We had a rescue jumper (who was shooting a video) and he was really keen to go… but while he was experienced, he had no experience of jumping into sea ice. The bow of the ship was ripped open and we feared the two men, now in the water, would get sucked into the ship. We got the basket down really quickly and the chief engineer got in. I have never seen anybody move so fast! When we went in again to pick up the skipper, he had a block of ice on top of him, but he managed to free himself and make it into the basket. We had made it with just five minutes of fuel to spare.'

Salty tales

In our everyday lives, we all know that salt has something to do with different degrees of the coldness of ice, even if we're not sure what. Georgian and Victorian housewives – who loved ice-cream at summer parties – knew that if salt was mixed with chipped ice in the outer freezing part of ice-cream churns, the ice-cream would freeze much faster. Even today, you can buy ice-cream makers with instructions for this salt-ice mixture. Local councils spread salt on roads to dissolve black ice – while we, on a smaller scale, do the same to make our doorsteps safe. All these examples tell us that salt water freezes at a higher temperature than fresh water.

Sailors discovered this when they hit a 'dead zone' when first voyaging into polar seas, even though the wind and waves were with them. They thought their ships were being held back by sea serpents or giant ice monsters, not understanding that the amount of fresh water dissolving from icebergs was diluting the salty seawater and making it less dense, or buoyant – with the result that their ships seemed heavier and sank lower in the water. Today, we understand better how air and sea temperature regulates salinity in relation to ice and icebergs. In fact, typical salt water is 35 parts of mineral salts in solution per thousand parts of water. This varies around the world. The Baltic Sea, with more fresh water in it, is less salty, while the Red Sea, which is warmer and evaporates faster, is saltier – and ships seem more buoyant.

Once in the helicopter, the two men were treated for hypothermia. Even in survival suits, the extreme cold of the water had taken its toll – but it was the suits that had protected them from certain death.

This is an example of how surface and aerial resources work well together to rescue ships and crews in distress. According to pilot Laura Guth: 'I've worked all over the east coast and the west coast of the US and the Bering Sea is undeniably the worst, especially in winter. It is so large, so cold and so rough that fishing vessels are often lost and sometimes we never even find the wreckage.'

Icy Death on the Scallop Draggers

Fishermen watch the sea and the sky more closely than most. Especially if they fish in the Grand Banks on Canada's Eastern Seaboard.

In summer, warm air and cool sea combine to make dense fogs that shroud the fishing grounds, causing many collisions. In winter, the sea freezes as soon as it hits the deck, adding incredible weight in ice. Both can sink a ship.

It takes a special kind of man to take to the sea, a sea that famously plays with men until their hearts are broken and wears stout ships to death.

Given the violent, icy weather of the Arctic seas off Nova Scotia, scallop-dragging is tough physical work. Two giant 15-foot rakes or draggers are lowered to the floor of the ocean

Freeze scale

This table shows the relationship between temperature and salinity in the seas.

Temperature	Effect
4° C	Non-salt water is at maximum density (has less air in it – achieved by convection cooling) and has potential to freeze.
0° C	Non-salt water freezes.
-1.3° C	Water more than 24.7 parts of salts per thousand parts of water freezes.
-8° C	The first minerals start to be deposited out of frozen seawater, gradually working their way down to the sea beneath the ice.
-23° C	Common salt is deposited down out of ice towards the sea water on which it is floating – gradually making ice and icebergs less salty until eventually they are pure, drinkable water.
-23° C and below	An iceberg (which is now made of pure water) is very hard. It is also very buoyant – which is why such great masses can float so easily.

on each side of the boat, dragged about in the mud, then hauled back and emptied. The buckets of scallops are carried off and the succulent white meat is scraped from the shell. The rakes go over the side again – as soon as one haul is processed the next load will be there; and this cycle goes on with no respite, day and night. The machinery is spring-loaded and heavy, and is operated as freezing sea spray whistles through the air. The temperatures are below freezing, the winds howling and waves as high as houses can be part of the package.

Over 600 Lunenberg fishermen have lost their lives at sea since records began in 1925. While boats have sunk and lives have been lost in the five years since the *Cape Aspy* disaster, it was this tragedy which has had the greatest effect on the community in recent history.

On 30 January 1993 the *Cape Aspy*, a 120-foot scallop dragger, left Lunenberg on the Nova Scotia coast. It was a dangerous time to go, with a rough sea and worsening weather, but there was financial pressure to get a catch.

The crew members who today survive – eleven of the original sixteen – estimate the temperature at minus 15 degrees Celsius once they were out at sea. Sea spray ice, always a major hazard for these fishermen, began to build up on the upper structure of the boat, on the side facing the wind. It is a sight of rare, deadly beauty, each drop of salty ice growing organically on the last, creating heavy, strange-shaped icicles that weigh a boat down and down. As *Cape Aspy* became asymmetrically top-heavy, it listed, took in water through its open hatches and on the deck, water which flooded down into the hull and across into the wheelhouse and engine room. Within six minutes, *Cape Aspy* lost power, was plunged in darkness, tipped and sank.

Several men reacted fast to put on their survival suits when the boat began to list and water started coming in. Randy Feener, one of the crew, made the suits a priority for himself and anyone he could grab.

'I put on my suit which took maybe thirty seconds and went up in the wheelhouse and the Master didn't have a suit on yet. I told him to go back and put a suit on and I would proceed putting out maydays. I put out probably two or three and there was no response so I figured that the aerials were probably iced up and bent over. I had a choice, I could either put a couple more maydays or go out on deck to try to get that organized. Water was coming up through the wheelhouse... one fella came up and he didn't have a suit so I dragged him back into a little room to get an extra suit... there was a little bit of confusion. I grabbed a hand-held beeper and while I was going out to where they were trying to get the liferaft I slipped on the ice and it [the beeper] went down in the water... I was just about to inflate the raft and a wave came up and washed me right over the side. I came up out of the water, I had a mouthful of water and I was disorientated. The whole of the boat was rolling over, I saw a fella fly off the hull. I tried to make for the liferaft but once the canopy inflated it acted as a sail and pushed the raft away faster than I could get to it.

'The survival suits are designed to bob you on top of the water. You blow up your pillow and bob but what I was finding was that the wind was going through me 'cos it was a cold night – the coldest night of the year, matter of fact. The wind was chilling my body so I decided instead of going horizontal in the water to go vertical and put the wind to my back because the wind under water was warmer.'

Murray Gurney was the skipper of the *T.K. Pierce*, the fishing boat which picked up ten members of the crew of the *Cape Aspy* from a liferaft. He encountered conditions that night as between 45 and 50 knot winds, too windy to fish. In fact, he had made up his mind to abandon fishing and return to Lunenburg when he got the distress call. He turned his boat around and headed for the spot. When they arrived on the scene, they couldn't see anything but could smell oil and soon they spotted oil slicks on the water. They searched for a couple of hours before seeing a flare. They kept losing their way in the falling snow and while they could see the red glow from flares in the sky, couldn't determine the direction they were coming from.

The waves must have been 40 feet high. A couple of men were visible in the liferaft, so cold that their faces were blue. Most of them had nothing on underneath their survival suits. They had been in their bunks when the boat started to go down and didn't have time to get dressed in warm clothing.

When Gurney learned that six more men were in the water, he got on to Harold Moore, skipper of the *Earnest Pierce*. Luckily, the boat soon found Randy Feener. Gurney and his men found two more bodies – but two were never recovered. The crew had the dismal experience of pulling into the wharf where many people were waiting for news.

Feener was six hours in the water. He kept his mind on his family, his wife and year-old son – and the positive things about his situation. Some might say the miracle was that he could find anything positive to think of, in one of the coldest seas in the world, unable to reach the lifeboat that danced so tantalizingly away from him, not knowing if they were being looked for.

'I probably could have survived another hour or two hours. My thumbs were starting to freeze so I popped them under my clothes. I knew that was a sign – like a house, you turn off the heat, you got so many hours before the house gets cold. The heat was going and there was no way I could regenerate it because the water of course was taking it away. I had a hundred and ten per cent faith in myself. I wanted to make sure that I survived 'cos the alternative ain't very good. You've gotta have a strong mind, a strong will.'

And, in such merciless waters, you also need all the help that modern science and technology can give you. Contrast Randy Feener's survival with the fate of a man who sailed with the crab fleet in the dreadful Bering Sea, summed up by Aleutian-based coast guard Captain Robert Wichlund as 'the most inhospitable place in the world'.

The man – without a survival suit – accidentally fell overboard and was recovered from the water in just *forty-five seconds*. In that short time, he had lost consciousness. From the moment he was scooped out of the sea by Captain Wichlund to his helicoptered arrival at hospital in St Paul, he was being given artificial respiration. He never recovered consciousness and died later that evening. The icy sea shows no mercy to the unfit or the unprepared.

chapter four

under pressure

Whales that can dive faster and deeper than any submarine; hard lessons learned through underwater disasters; divers who can hold their breath longer than doctors say is possible; huge pressures that can crush a nuclear submarine at a depth of 1,000 feet but don't damage delicate fish at 30,000 feet – air-breathing mankind has sought to understand and enter the world of water and stay there for ever longer periods at greater depths, the ultimate goal the deep chasms nearly seven miles below the surface of the sea.

Opposite Curiosity was Alexander the Great's driving force. The man who conquered the known world also wanted to conquer the sea. A student of Aristotle, he ordered a diving barrel to be made so he could sit on the bottom of the Aegean and wonder at the fascinating world beneath the waves.

We are beautifully designed to work at normal air pressure at sea level. Our bodies struggle at extremes of height; mountain climbers and balloonists find it hard to breathe in thin air. We cannot exist without artificial aids under water because we have to breathe air. Unable to cope with the immense pressure forces, the sheer weight of water below about 1,000 feet would crush us. Even sea creatures in their natural environment can have problems with sudden changes of pressure. Because a fish does not have lungs, it can descend to astonishing depths, but needs time to adjust its swim bladder when going down or coming up. Certain body organs in creatures dredged from great depths in scientific experiments explode; for them, going *upwards* is a mirror image of us going *down*.

However, air-breathing whales and seals can dive at great speed to great depths – and how they endure the tremendous pressure changes involved in dives of several hundred fathoms is not definitely known. They are warm-blooded mammals like ourselves. Caisson disease, which is caused by the rapid accumulation of nitrogen bubbles in the blood with sudden release of pressure, kills human divers. Yet, according to the testimony of whalers, a baleen whale when harpooned can dive straight down to a depth of half a mile, as measured by the amount of line carried out. From these depths, where it has sustained pressure of half a ton on every inch of its body, it returns almost immediately to the surface.

The plausible explanation is that, unlike the diver, who has air pumped to him while he is under water, the whale has in its body only the limited supply it carries down and does not have enough nitrogen in its blood to do serious harm. When it dives deep, its lungs and windpipe partially collapse. The contained air rushes into nonabsorptive passages in its head and the whale then uses oxygen stored in its red blood and muscle cells. The heartbeat slows to about one-third of the usual rate; body temperature and metabolic rate drop and blood leaves the extremities (flippers, skin, tail) to enrich the heart and brain. As the whale rises, the air stored in its head re-enters the lungs and it is this air which is blown so hard at the surface.

The greatest depth at which a sperm whale has been found entangled with underwater telephone cables was 620 fathoms or nearly two-thirds of a mile. They have all been found with the cable in their mouths and their subsequent struggles have twisted the cable around their great bodies, eventually drowning them. More whales have been trapped by cables at about 500 fathoms than any other depth, suggesting that the natural food of the sperm whale may be concentrated at about this

li aparuist en macedone en
la samblance quil li deust
aidier quil peust retorner
sain et sauf a son peuple
non mie por lui · ançes por le

lauuement deaus · Lors
a ombra la uertu diuine ·

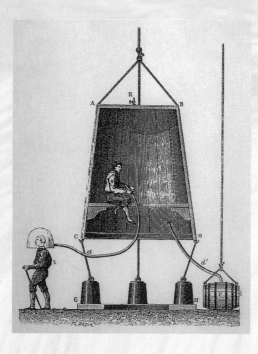

The man who named a comet also wanted to say he had seen the wonders of the deep. In 1690 Edmund Halley devised the first real diving bell filled with air which was gently lowered with weights. One of Halley's divers actually walked a short distance on the sea bed with a small wooden air-filled cask on his head, inaccurately shown here as a glass jar.

level – and that they were dredging the bottom with mouths open. But again, we just don't know the answers.

In 1979 marine biologist Sylvia Earle, at the time chief scientist at the National Oceanographic and Atmosphere Administration in Washington, made a record-breaking solo walk on the ocean floor at a depth of 1,250 feet. In 1994 she said in an interview in *Science News*: 'Earth is a marine habitat... The ocean is home to the greatest diversity of the planet. It's still ironic that there are more footprints on the moon than there are on the bottom of the sea, and we're only seven miles away . . .' Later she was to elaborate: 'There's a perception that we have already explored the sea. The reality is that we know more about Mars than we know about the oceans.'

The undersea world has long fascinated us. From earliest times, man has tried to peer through the veil, from the fourth century BC when Aristotle described a primitive diving bell: 'So that sponge fishers may be supplied with air for respiration, vases are lowered in the water with the mouth downwards so they fill not with water, but with air; these vases are forced steadily down, held perfectly upright, for if tipped slightly, the water enters and knocks it over . . .' While Alexander the Great, so avidly curious about the known world that he tried to conquer it, in 333 BC sat beneath the Aegean Sea in a 'glass barrel' or a glass-sided cage through which he saw whales and all manner of denizens of the deep, according to legend. By 1690 the astronomer, Edmund Halley, had invented the first diving bell – although divers could see absolutely nothing except their feet. Divers sat in a wooden cask with an open bottom. As the cask was lowered, the air inside was squashed by rising water so extra air was somehow added from wooden barrels. Divers could walk outside the bell with small casks over their heads – though what they could possibly achieve, or for how long, has never been told.

The earliest frogman was possibly Sultan Ghazi Chelebi, described by the Turkish author Ibn Battuta in his *Travels* in 1332: 'The Sultan was a brave and audacious man, with a peculiar capacity for swimming underwater. He used to sail out with his war vessels to fight against Greeks, and when the fleets met and everyone was occupied with the fighting, he would dive under the water carrying an iron tool with which he pierced the enemy's ships, and they knew nothing about it until all at once they sank.'

Penetrating the depths to more than a few hundred feet has always been the ultimate adventure of the planet – possibly the last great adventure. We've climbed the highest mountains, we have ventured into the rain forests, paddled canoes up and down the Amazon, waged war in the Sahara desert – blown up remote Pacific atolls with the atom bomb; but still, we haven't walked on the bottom of the ocean abyss.

A very few people have come as close as is possible. On 23 January 1960 Jacques Piccard and Lt Don Walsh made 'the deepest dive for mankind' by descending almost seven miles in the bathyscaph, *Trieste*, to the bottom of the Challenger Deep. This is a terrifying hole in the 1,580-mile long Marianas Trench, some 200 miles off Guam, named for *Challenger II*, the British ship that first found it in 1851 – destroying all preconceptions that the bottom of the sea was a flat, featureless place only a few thousand feet below the surface.

A Swiss national, Piccard was already familiar with the concept of deep exploration, aware that only 2 per cent of the floor of the entire world ocean is deeper than 6,000 metres. His father, Auguste, a Zurich professor, had long had a dream of seeing undamaged fishes brought up entire from thousands of feet below the surface. In 1905, as a young student, Auguste read a book that attempted to describe unknown fishes dredged from the bottom of the ocean, but which, by the time they came to the surface, were mostly destroyed by the rapid increase in pressure.

Jacques Piccard says: 'My father told me, it's the wrong way to do it, but if you like to see how fishes are, you must descend yourself, you know, and go into the deep water.' Auguste Piccard, a balloonist, got the idea of attaching a sphere to a huge cylinder filled with a kind of gasoline that is lighter than water and compressible with increased depth. For many years Professor Piccard's invention

was just a dream, interrupted by two world wars; but eventually, he was supported by the Belgium National Science Foundation, which enabled him to build an unmanned, unattached submersible vessel, FNRS-2 (Fonds National de la Recherche Scientifique) which descended to 4,554 feet in 1948 off Dakar in West Africa, a record plunge. On the deck of the support vessel was the inventor of the aqualung, Jacques Cousteau.

Encouraged, Auguste and Jacques Piccard managed to raise sufficient funds to build *Trieste* (named after the Adriatic port where she was constructed). The 50-foot-long flotation hull was designed to hold 28,000 gallons of gasoline. Suspended below it was the 'globe', a 120-ton forged steel chamber, 7 feet in inside diameter, designed to hold two passengers. The portholes were 6-inch-thick truncated cones made of a newly developed, shatterproof plastic called Plexiglas. Functioning like an up-down

Top Jacques Piccard and US Navy lieutenant Don Walsh wave from the bathyscaphe *Trieste* on 23 January 1960 after emerging from their record-breaking dive 35,797 feet to the bottom of the Marianas Trench off Guam – a record that has never been surpassed.

Above 1953: the *Trieste* is lowered into the shallow waters of Castellamare harbour, Italy, as Swiss Professor Auguste Piccard runs tests on the bathyscaph he built and designed with his son, Jacques.

Deeper and deeper

1934
William Beebe and Otis Barton reached a depth of 3,028 feet off Bermuda in a bathysphere.

1949
Otis Barton descended to 4,500 feet off California in a steel sphere known as the benhoscope.

1953
Auguste and Jacques Piccard descend to 10,395 feet in the Mediterranean in the bathyscaph, the *Trieste*.

1954
Georges Houot and Pierre-Henri Willm descend to 13,287 feet off the coast of Africa in the FNRS-3.

1960
Jacques Piccard and Don Walsh descend to a record 35,797 feet in the Marianas Trench off Guam in the *Trieste*.

At 26,000 feet the pressure on the *Trieste* was 150,000 tons; at 35,797 feet it was 200,000 tons, equal to 300 tons per square metre; or overall, the equivalent of the weight of five battleships pressing down.

elevator, in August 1953 with both Piccards aboard, *Trieste* made her first successful manned descent off Castellamare in southern Italy – to the bottom of the harbour, a mere 26 feet that nevertheless proved she was watertight. Deeper test dives eventually led to testing at 10,300 feet in the Tyrrhenian Sea. Having proved it would work, but unable to finance it any longer, Auguste Piccard sold *Trieste* to the US Office of Naval Research, but he and his son were asked to continue with their work.

Finally, the younger Piccard and Lt Walsh were ready for the deepest dive of all; but it was a dive that nearly didn't get made: a blink away from the *Trieste* leaving for her record-breaking dive, the ONR got cold feet because so much money was being spent by them on rockets that kept blowing up. Admiral Burke declared he couldn't justify a dive that he felt had few chances of succeeding.

'I told him we are going to the deepest part of the ocean,' Jacques Piccard says, 'and he said, "I don't want to hear this, I have been promised too many things." Then he relented with the memorable words, "But don't tell anyone."' The admiral had quite a droll sense of humour. When Piccard asked him how deep the new nuclear submarines could go, he replied, 'It is absolutely forbidden for me to tell you this most important secret. No, I cannot tell you for any reason – but if you really need to know, ask either the New York *Times* or the Russian Embassy and they will be glad to tell you.'

But despite this, when the *Trieste* was actually over the Challenger Deep, getting ready to dive, a message was received from Washington by the mother ship, the *Lewis*, ordering the dive to be cancelled. Chief Petty Officer John Michelle quietly pocketed the message from the radio officer – and went out to assist in the preparations.

Despite the previous tests and the careful preparation, no one knew how *Trieste* would actually stand up to going down to a depth four times deeper than ever tried before. Jacques had plenty of confidence.

'We knew that it could not explode; the pressure outside was too big, and it could not crush because the pressure tests in laboratories showed us the sphere was all right. There were some unknown things. We could have, for instance, landed in a place full of rocks and crevasses and have difficulty with the small local geology... We decided to go very slowly, then if something mysterious happens, we know and we go up.

'You can think of the ocean as a layer cake, many different layers as you go down. Most people know that the surface of the ocean has certain circulations like the Gulf Stream and surface currents, but that's not all there is. As you go below the surface, you begin to run into other circulation patterns, deep circulation patterns.'

Ten minutes after leaving the surface, the bathyscaph stopped of its own volition at 300 feet. They had reached a much colder layer of water and the relative weight of the craft with respect to the water had suddenly diminished, bringing the descent to a halt. When the gasoline cooled they would continue – but that would waste valuable time. So, hoping they were doing the right thing, Piccard and Walsh released some of the gasoline and continued downwards until 35 feet later another cool layer stopped them. They were to stop and start three more times in this way, to a depth of 650 feet, each time releasing the gasoline to continue down. From then on, the coldness did not increase perceptively, thus proving wrong those who were convinced that the entire bottom of the ocean was frozen solid. It was while they were stopped in suspense at each cold 'ceiling' that Piccard noticed the marked presence of the thermocline, internal waves that caused them to gently rise and fall like a boat lulled on the surface of a gentle sea.

Even on the brightest day with the sun directly overhead, light fades out rapidly in the sea. The red rays are gone at the end of the first 200–300 feet, and with them, all the warmth of the colour of the sun. Then the greens fade away until at 1,000 feet only a deep, dark brilliant blue is left. In very clear waters, the violet of the spectrum might remain for another 100 feet. By 1,500 feet the darkness is total: you have entered the almost solid, unrelieved blackness of the undersea world, a darkness so extreme that it is hard to describe. For Piccard and Walsh as they entered this zone of eternal night, the first traces of phosphorescent plankton appeared.

At that time it was believed, because of soundings, that the ocean has a kind of false bottom. In fact, the Russians had told Piccard that he was a fool to think he would land easily on the bottom. They suggested he would be swallowed up by some kind of obscure soup, a primeval ooze which could be 50 or 100 feet deep, maybe more. The thing is, nobody knew what to expect (and indeed, they still don't – seventeen years after *Trieste*'s descent such strange phenomena as deep sea vents and black smokers were discovered – see page 194 – and there are many more wonders still waiting). In fact, the bottom turned out to be quite solid and easy to settle on. There was a considerable quantity of a white talc-like material, possibly consisting of diatoms – small marine creatures which had died and drifted slowly downwards over countless millions of years.

Piccard recalls the historic moment: 'Indifferent to the nearly 200,000 tons of pressure clamped on her metal sphere, the *Trieste* balanced herself delicately on the few pounds of guide rope that lay on the bottom, making token claim, in the name of science and humanity, to the ultimate depths in all our oceans – the Challenger Deep.'

They were at the bottom of the planet world at a depth of 35,797 feet. It was an incredible moment; but Piccard and Walsh were more moved by the sight of a flatfish, rather like a halibut or sole, which had drifted into sight in their mercury vapour lights – and, even more startling, it was a fish with eyes in depths which were suffocatingly dark. At the very bottom of creation, in water seven miles deep, there was something that scientists said could not be: a real fish. As Piccard points out, 'It tells you that there is food, it tells you there is oxygen and it tells you there is current circulation... It tells you that high order fish can live at that great depth... Our fish was the instantaneous reply... to a question that thousands of oceanographers had been asking themselves for decades.'

It was unfortunate that Piccard and Walsh did not carry a camera because several eminent scientists immediately denied that they could have seen a fish at such a depth, somewhat smugly concluding that 'everyone agreed' the creature could only have been a sea cucumber. It was to be several years before Piccard and Walsh were proved right – that fishes do indeed exist at the bottom of the ocean.

At the moment of their triumph, Piccard recalls Walsh murmuring, 'We are at a depth where no one has yet been,' and his own response: 'Silently I acquiesce.'

The pressure had not crushed them, as some thought it might. But Piccard was always confident.

'We would not have been crushed. We would have water in the mouth of course; but the fishes when they are under water, they have the mouth open so they have the same pressure inside and outside, like everything would. Take a glass, just a normal crystal glass, and put it in the water. When you go deeper and deeper you have the pressure increasing inside and outside but the glass would not crush. The same for fish, the same for man. Fishes adapt much better than man because [of their swim bladder]. Man has to be in a strong sphere resistant to pressure that takes us one or two years to build – while the fish have had millions of years to adapt.'

Rachel Carson summed it up in her eloquent book, *The Sea Around Us*: 'At first thought it seems a paradox that creatures of such great fragility as the glass sponge and the jellyfish can live under the conditions of immense pressure that prevail in deep water. For creatures at home in the sea, however, the saving fact is that the pressure inside their tissues is the same as that without, and, as long as this balance is preserved, they are no more inconvenienced by a pressure of a ton or so than we are by ordinary atmospheric pressure.'

Our problem is that we need to breathe air and it is the unequal pressure of that inside our bodies which prevents us from swimming freely at any real depth. Free divers, who have learned to empty their lungs of oxygen, have made dives as much as 500 feet (see page 162). It is the amount of air trapped inside which crumples submarines like paper when they dive below their depth, causing so many tragedies over the years. The worst submarine disaster on record occurred on 10 April 1963 when the US nuclear submarine *Thresher* sank off New Hampshire with her crew of 129. It is believed that a leak in the hull short-circuited the transformer, shutting off the nuclear reactor. Without power, the submarine sank to a depth of 1,400 fathoms, where extreme pressure collapsed the hull.

On *Trieste*, Piccard and Walsh checked the external temperature – at 37.4 degrees Fahrenheit, proving that while it does get colder the deeper you go, at a certain point the temperature levels off – and established that the bottom of the sea was not in fact

frozen (or even consisting of soup!). The two men thereupon unfurled their respective nations' flags and ate a chocolate bar apiece (one Swiss, one American) before releasing a magnetic current that allowed two tons of iron-pellet ballast to drop to the bottom and beginning the ascent. They had lingered on the bottom for just twenty minutes – twenty-seven times deeper than a conventional submarine could go. The entire journey there and back lasted for just under eight and a half hours.

Of his journey to the bottom of the world, Piccard says: 'I was glad for my father because he invented the bathyscaph. We built it together. It demonstrated that man is able to go to any place in the ocean.'

Since that day in 1948 when Jacques Cousteau had watched the descent of the Piccards' FNRS-2, he had desired a submersible of his own as a window in the sea to study its flora and fauna. In 1954 Cousteau finally achieved his wish, entering the sea in FNRS-3, sponsored by l'Office Français de Recherches Sous-Marines (OFRS), launching from the *Elie Monnier*, the very ship from which he had watched the Piccards.

Cousteau saw a bright red squid ejecting clouds of luminous white ink at 4,000 feet; on the bottom he saw 8-foot-long sharks with bright green eyes. Falling in love with so much enchantment, Cousteau and his son went on to build DS-2, a diving saucer which they nicknamed *La soucoupe plongeante*, a flattened sphere six and a half feet in diameter and five feet high, with two viewing windows – not to mention space enough to 'loll on mattresses like Romans at a banquet'. Unlike previous submersibles, D2-2 was equipped with jet nozzles that could move her in any direction and even spin her on her horizontal axis, so she could be tilted up and down as well. The finishing touch was cameras that were synchronized with a flash unit mounted

US atomic submarine the *Thresher*, which sank in 1963 at a depth of 1,400 fathoms with the loss of 129 men. The tremendous pressure at that depth crushed the submarine like an eggshell.

Above Jacques Cousteau, inventor of the scuba-diving equipment, teaches his young son Jean how to use it.

Right Jacques Cousteau in the submersible he irreverently nicknamed '*La soucoupe plongeante*' – the diving saucer.

outside the hull, designed by Harold Edgerton, the inventor of stroboscopic photography.

Cousteau was to go on to build submersibles that would go even deeper – *Deepstar*, and *Deepstar-4000*, designed with battery-powered propellers – from which he was to see (but for some reason not to photograph) a fish '30 or 40 feet long with an eye the size of a dinner plate' in the San Diego Trough. No one knew what it was, although suggestions were advanced that it was a Greenland or sleeper shark; however, they grow to a maximum of 23 feet and have eyes the size of silver dollars.

Enthusiasm for exploring the unknown oceans grew. Scientists and nations were almost racing to design and launch submersibles, with countries such as Japan joining in for the first time.

The rewards are not just to explore the unknown, to be the first to come across that elusive undersea monster – but to be the first in a race that equals finding oil in Alaska or the Gold Rush in California; for the bottom of the oceans are depositories of vast mineral wealth. Or perhaps someone will be the first to discover natural substances for use in medicine, or chemicals not yet thought of. Another lure is that massive ocean currents influence much of the world's weather patterns – unlocking their secrets would add to the knowledge of weather forecasters, possibly saving billions of dollars in weather-related disasters.

Cities of the future sit waiting on the drawing board for the funding and the technology to catch up with vision. Conshelf I, the first underwater home for divers, was invented by Jacques Cousteau in 1962. Two divers spent a week in it at a depth of 33 feet. The United States designed Sealab and Tektite, two undersea environments in which scientists have lived at depths of 660 feet for up to thirty days at a time.

More than thirty-five years after *Trieste*, *Deep Flight I*, a revolutionary undersea vessel, shaped like a chubby, 12-foot winged torpedo that can fly like a bird through the water to incredible depths, has recently been built by British inventor and engineer Graham Hawkes. A skilled pilot lying horizontally, head protruding into the vessel's glass nose, can perform barrel rolls like dolphins, race a pod of whales, or even leap vertically right out of the water. Waiting in the wings to perform more miracles for science is *Deep Flight II* – capable of diving seven miles straight down.

Recently, soundings have found that the deepest part of Challenger Deep is 378 feet deeper than had been thought. It is 36,175 feet – a record that Graham Hawkes intends to make in *Deep Flight II*. The mini-sub is extremely light, weighing less than water, and is designed not only to withstand massive pressures but to swim like a whale through them. According to Hawkes, with reference to the fact that Piccard and Walsh's flatfish was at first derided by much of the establishment: 'This is raw planetary exploration. We have been to Mars, we have been to the moon and we don't know whether there are fish at the bottom of the ocean. I am going down there to see if there is a fish – it's as basic as that.'

Hawkes has calculated that pressure is the biggest obstacle. At 4,000 feet the total pressure on the nose cone of *Deep Flight* is 1.6 million pounds. At 7 miles it would be 13 million pounds. According to him, the key to success is the new materials, particularly ceramics, designed by the US Navy. *Deep Flight* has been tested off Mexico to a depth of 4,000 feet, where it was found that the principal problem was not pressure but speed. The little submarine moves as fast as a manta ray, which causes the pilot to lose sight of his visual horizons – the bottom or the top – thus losing

Deep Flight 1 – British engineer Graham Hawkes's streamlined submarine that can manoeuvre like a dolphin underwater. The pilot lies in a horizontal position with his head in the glass dome for maximum visibility.

control. If the pilot slows too much, like a conventional plane, it will stall – but instead of dropping, the force of reverse gravity lets it float back up to the surface. The frustrating thing about the Mexico test was that Hawkes would spot some fascinating creatures and overtake them, leaving them somewhere in his wake. He wants to be able to cruise level with them, to study them in their environment. He talks of his submarine flying, not swimming, through the sea. To him it's like a spaceship coming in to a new planet – only the planet is the bottom of the ocean on planet Earth, not one somewhere out in the far reaches of space.

The *Truculent* Disaster

In 1950 a Royal Navy submarine, the *Truculent*, had just completed a refit at Chatham Dockyards, ready to undergo surface trials on 12 January and diving trials the next day, the 13th. Because of superstition, the trials were changed around, with the diving first. On board were the crew of sixty or so and about twenty dock workers.

Everything went well, despite a few minor engine problems, and everyone was sitting down to a meal on the way home when the engine stopped. Although they were on the surface, the escape procedure was put into effect as a precaution. At the time, they were in the wide mouth of the Thames Estuary, close to the sea. Without warning, and in thick fog, the *Truculent* was hit by a small Swedish merchant ship, fitted with ice-breakers on its bow. Part of the submarine was sliced away and it started to sink in

British submarine HMS *Truculent* being salvaged in the Thames estuary, where she sank with the loss of 64 lives after a surface collision in the fog.

80 feet of water. They thought they had hit a mine.

Les Stickland was an engineer in charge of the diving and escape equipment. He was the first to the engine room when the engine stopped. At first, it never occurred to him that they would actually have to make an escape. At that point, he was following the procedure. 'It's something we never even considered, something you never thought would happen... you ruled it out almost entirely.'

But when the submarine started to sink so rapidly, Stickland went to the blowing panel and blew the tanks, trying to stabilize the boat long enough for everybody to get back into the engine room and after compartments which were isolated from the flooded part of the vessel. They managed to do this in the twenty seconds available before the boat settled on the bottom, but there was no time for the submarine to send out an SOS. The ship-to-shore on the Swedish ship was out of order, so it too could not radio for assistance.

Five of the submarine crew were on deck when the collision happened. They were washed away and were eventually picked up by a Dutch vessel, which raised the alarm, but the balance – seventy-four men – were trapped under the water in the submerged hull.

With so many people on board, oxygen was a major problem. No one seemed to know how much they had left, but all of them knew that they could not just sit there and wait to be rescued. They had to get out – but the escape hatch could not be opened while there was a massive weight of water pressing down on it, unequal to the lighter weight of air within the submarine. The escape procedure involved everyone waiting in the engine room while the air was blown out and the ballast chambers fully flooded until the inside pressure equalled the outside pressure. The air they needed to breathe had to be divided from the flooded escape capsule. This was done by lowering a kind of canvas trunk which came down from the hatch to below the surface of the water in the compartment, acting as a kind of watertight cut-off. Then the trunk was vented and flooded. The entire equalizing procedure took about an hour and a half.

During this time the DSEA (Davies Submarine Escape Apparatus) sets, normally enough for the crew but not for the large number of civilians on board, were allocated to non-swimmers and civilians, who were also quickly instructed in their use. Engine noises were heard above the submarine, which they thought must be rescue vessels waiting above – but sounds carry a long way under water, and the sounds they could hear were just those of normal commercial traffic at a distance in a busy seaway.

As soon as it was thought the pressure was equal, a crew member climbed through the canvas trunk to open the hatch. He was supposed to return to let everyone know it was open so they could take their turn to escape. However, he was caught in a mixture of air and water as it rushed upwards from the submarine that forced him to the surface. Eventually, someone went to check and found the hatch was open.

Fifty years ago, basic escape training was indeed very basic. There were seven to ten days of classroom lectures; and just one hour of immersion in a shallow tank using

The most valuable ballast ever?
Submarines need ballast to stay under water. In 1941, after unloading its cargo of emergency supplies at the battle zone of Corregidor, the submarine USS *Trout* took on a ballast of Philippine government gold bars worth $9 million (many more times that in today's value) in order to travel back to San Francisco safely under the surface.

DSEA gear, which was, remarkably, a plastic or rubber bag with a breathing tube and nose piece, as Stickland explains.

> '*All it did was give you sufficient air to get to the surface and on the surface it acted like a lifebelt. It simply doesn't compare with the present system, which gives complete protection from the weather, it gives buoyancy and it gives an absolute sense of security I am sure we didn't have.*
>
> '*We went out one by one. Those with the DSEA were again given a short briefing before they ducked under the water in the trunk; while those without DSEA sets just ducked under. They were told to gradually release their breath on their way up and wished the best of luck. Sam Hinds and myself were in the compartment to the end. We then came out when we were sure that everybody had left.*'

Stickland said that everyone had been very calm, very relaxed, with no sign of panic. They knew that they were in a difficult position, but all of them believed that since they were in such shallow water they would bob up like corks, with rescue boats waiting just 75 or 80 feet away above.

The first shock was the bitter cold. In the engine room, the sea water had mixed with hot oil from the engine, so everyone gained a false impression. In fact, it was the middle of January and the water was just one degree Fahrenheit above freezing. Stickland: 'The cold was the startling factor in the whole episode. It was a clear frosty night and visibility was perfect. The rise through the water was perfectly OK. When I got near the surface there was a moment or two of panic as you tend to think you are out of air before you hit the surface, but the first feeling on hitting the surface was one of tremendous elation. I felt over the moon.'

This sense of euphoria was quickly followed by the realization that something was radically wrong – Stickland could hear cries for help all around – and it became apparent that no help was available. There wasn't a rescue ship in sight. During the next forty minutes or so, friends and colleagues began to disappear. Out of the blue a rowing boat appeared. 'Probably the last thing I expected to see at that stage was a rowing boat. It turned out to be from the *Divina*, the ship that hit us. They didn't have a motor boat but they put down a rowing boat and it picked me up, together with two or three of the other survivors.'

Stickland had neither a DSEA set or a lifejacket, but he was a good swimmer, and rather on the plump side, a fact he believes helped keep out the cold. The outgoing tide and local current eddies were extremely fast, but since they had no land references they didn't realize how far they had been carried towards the sea.

Most people who died were too cold to survive. They were swept away and drowned. Three others died because they didn't release the pressure in their lungs sufficiently quickly and their lungs ruptured. 'But it is a natural tendency to hold one's breath until you reach the top – but that is fatal.' In all, sixty-four people died that night, with just fifteen survivors.

HMS *Dolphin*: Lessons in How to Escape

The first and most important lesson learned from the tragic loss of life in the *Truculent* is that training in submarine escape is absolutely vital. Over the past ninety years there have been more than 170 peacetime submarine losses and 85 per cent of those – as in the case of the *Truculent* – have occurred in relatively shallow water. It was after the *Truculent* disaster that the British Royal Navy started to take the mortality rate seriously by setting up a study into improving its submarine escape capability. Physical and psychological training was considered vital, with stress on the importance of pressurized ascent training. As a result, the Submarine Escape Training Tank – SETT – was constructed at HMS *Dolphin* in Portsmouth.

Brian Wood was in the Royal Navy for thirty-three years and has specialized in submarine escape and rescue since 1977. He left the Navy in 1995 but still works as a civilian instructor at SETT, helping to oversee the escape drills which all submariners have to go through. If they fail, they are sent back to surface ships. Wood has performed real escape drills from eight different submarines. He vividly recalls his first ever series of escapes in 1977 from a submarine submerged near the Kyle of Lochalsh in Scotland. There were three escapes from different depths, culminating in one from 440 feet.

'It's cold and dark down there, there are no instructors to talk to, you're on your own... but it's quite exhilarating, the adrenaline rush is greater than parachute jumping.'

Sea-based submarine escapes normally take place from a submarine submerged to a depth of between 300 and 600 feet. Wood was part of the Royal Navy team which set the world record escape depth of 601 feet in a Norwegian fjord in 1987. But that's not the limit. The Navy is investigating training for escape from the new Trident class of submarine which would involve drills from as deep as 1,000 feet. In theory, an escape could be made using SETT suits from as deep as 2,000 feet – but so far, it's just a theory.

The design of the suits – a far cry from the primitive DSEA set – is vital. Escapees wear a specially designed suit with a built-in lifejacket. The escape suits have an air supply inside them that allows the escapee to breathe normally on his ascent to the suface. As he rises to the surface, this air supply is fed by the change in pressure. Excess air is dissipated through relief valves and the hood of his suit. There is a real risk that if you don't breathe out your lungs will rupture – again, something that wasn't really recognized in the *Truculent* disaster, when people simply wanted to hold their breath for as long as possible.

The SETT tank is 30 metres deep, and trainees gradually work up to that depth. For safety, instructors (who have no diving equipment) wait in the water just outside the

Top Showing relief on being rescued, Les Stickland (fourth from the left) and some of the fifteen survivors of the *Truculent* warm up with cups of hot tea. Sixty-four of their companions were not so lucky: limited escape training and equipment, freezing water and strong currents in the Thames estuary where the submarine sank combined to take their lives.

Above Les Stickland, a survivor of the 1950 *Truculent* submarine disaster, today watches escape training drills at SETT, HMS *Dolphin*, the British Navy's submarine escape training school.

escape hatch. The most difficult part of the process is just before the escape hatch is opened when the escapee has to adjust to the sudden change in pressure as the air breathed in is balanced to the pressure of the water outside. 'Climbing into the chamber is like getting into the barrel of a gun. The hatch is shut, air is fed into your lifejacket slightly above the ambient pressure in the escape tower. Then the flood valve opens, the chamber fills with water, the hatch above opens, and you're away, rapidly ascending through a spectrum of colours.'

But on a sea drill you are on your own from the moment you enter the hatch until you reach the surface. Once through the hatch you will shoot to the surface, exhaling furiously throughout the rapid ascent at a rate of 10–14 feet a second, aided by 70 pounds of positive buoyancy supplied by the air in the suit, hood and lifejacket. 'You're so relieved to get out of the escape tower, a relief that you're still alive' is the general feeling.

Medics and instructors wait on the surface and there is always a recompression chamber should it be required. Many people, especially instructors attempting their first real escape, have nightmares in the run-up to the experience. 'He'll be talking to his mum, God, and anyone else that will listen.' A few back out at the last minute.

There are three reasons why water pressure presents a real danger to people trying to escape from a submarine. The first one is a practical one: they can't open the hatch to escape. At a depth of 10 metres there is a pressure of 2 kilos per square centimetre. At a depth of 50 metres, it is 6 kilos per square centimetre. This is the equivalent of a submarine's hatch having three and a half tonnes of water pressure pushing down on it at about 30 metres. It is therefore necessary to equalize the pressure inside the submarine to that outside it, by letting the water *in* and blowing the air *out*.

Secondly, the lungs are affected. When you take a breath of air at the surface, you are taking it in at one bar pressure; at 30 metres below the surface, that same breath of air is four times greater. As you rise up through the water on your way to the surface, the air in your lungs expands – and if it can't expand outwards through your mouth or nose (because you are holding your breath) your lungs could rupture.

Early submariners had only the very basic DSEA set available when things went wrong. It was the *Truculent* disaster which led to more research and development in this vital field.

The third reason is the danger of decompression illness or the 'bends'– an extremely painful and often fatal affliction. This can sometimes be a hazard for submarine escapees because of the potentially rapid change in pressure which they experience between leaving the submarine and reaching the surface. For scuba divers, however, decompression illness is a more major concern. Divers breathe air underwater that is pressurized to the depth at which they are diving. If divers surface too fast, the decrease in pressure can affect the nitrogen gas that is absorbed into their bloodstream. The nitrogen can form bubbles in the blood which block the blood's flow. Divers often use special computers which tell them how long they should spend underwater at a certain depth and how quickly they can ascend. If divers get the 'bends' they must go into recompression chambers to

A diver in a modern SETT suit trains in an escape tank at HMS *Dolphin*. Compare this state of the art equipment with the somewhat primitive DSEA pack.

dissolve these potentially lethal nitrogen bubbles. Often, they may have to remain there for several days, depending on how ill they are and how long they spent underwater.

Someone who has discovered from personal experience how painful the bends can be is a scallop diver, Paul Camilli.

The Scallop Diver

Paul Camilli lives in the remote and beautiful Scottish island of Raasay; for a living he dives in the cold offshore waters for scallops (or clams, as they are known in some parts of the world). In certain areas of the world, particularly the Georges Banks of the United States, clams are dredged up by the ton and there is no doubt that this is very damaging to the environment. Camilli describes himself as 'a hunter-gatherer living on the edge'. The way in which he works is ecologically sound and avoids destroying the sea bed. 'The beauty of it is that all I have to do is put a suit on and jump in the water,' he says.

However, it can be personally dangerous: 'With every dive there is a risk, with each dive that risk gets greater, particularly with age.'

He has a computer that tells him how much air he has left, how long his decompression time should be, but sometimes – especially in the summer when the weather is fine – he is so enchanted by the world under water that he can almost forget where he is.

'I am restricted by my decompression times and by my air capacity and by the temperature... 40 minutes down at 30 metres where the water may be only 8 or 9 degrees Celsius is enough – your hands dropping off [with cold] but you just get tunnel vision and all you can see are scallops.

'The deeper you go, the less time you have because the more nitrogen you absorb in your blood stream. The oxygen goes in and out of your bloodstream just fine; but the nitrogen comes out slower. If you rise too quickly, it comes out in the form of bubbles which can get trapped in various parts of the body, the brain, heart, joints, spine. It can give you a bad case of pins and needles – or it can kill you.'

In September 1997, Camilli suffered from the bends. Initially he tried to ignore the pain in his arm, but then it became too much to bear. Since it was his arm, he didn't think it would cause much damage, although he has known people paralysed from the waist down and confined to wheelchairs when the nitrogen bubble has shifted to their spine. 'I did a stupid thing. I should have gone straight to the coast guard and alerted them because I could have died.'

Instead, Camilli did another unwise thing – he went back into the water to see if he could decompress himself. It's true the pain did ease – but, as soon as he surfaced, it was worse. In the end, the pain was so excruciating that he became delirious with it. That night a helicopter was scrambled and he was lifted off to the decompression chamber at Kishorn on the mainland. On the way, the pains spread to other areas of his body and he imagined the bubbles going to his heart or lungs. As soon as he got inside the chamber it was like going from 'agony to euphoria'.

The experience taught him how fragile life was. He had received such a shock that he didn't dive for three months and gradually eased back into it because he had been missing it so much.

Remarkably, there is a large group of divers who have such a natural affinity for water that the bends are not a concern. This is because they are breath-hold or free divers. True water babies like the Cuban Francisco 'Pippin' Ferraras, the Italian Umberto Pelizzari and the American Mehgan Heaney-Grier have been taking diving science beyond its known and accepted limits.

Testing the Limits

For a group of unusual human mermaids and mermen, freedom is a dive away. They have no air, no equipment other than a pair of fins and gulp in just one deep breath as they head like arrows towards the bottom of the blue sea. They come from a long line of free divers, going back some 5,000 years.

Some of the first human divers were pearl and sponge collectors. Pearls have been gathered in the Arabian Gulf since at least 3000 BC, where early divers wore turtle-shell nose clips to keep water out of their nostrils. With no equipment but with practice they could dive perhaps 66–100 feet and stay under for several minutes on a single breath. Even today, on the island of Kalymnos in Greece, a few poorly equipped *sfougarades*, or

'naked' sponge divers, wear no breathing equipment and use a stone to anchor themselves to the bottom in what is called the 'man-eating profession' – one that has killed over 100 men and severely damaged many others, the biggest danger being 'shallow-water blackout'.

As a child in Milan, Umberto Pelizzari cried in the shower, frightened that he might drown. He refused to bathe in the sea during family holidays, hiding instead in the shade of a beach umbrella – and if that

Early divers search for sponges in the sea off Crete without any artificial aids other than the brick they hold to take them to the bottom. The mortality rate from the bends was high.

wasn't enough, he had a heart murmur. This is the same man who today is acknowledged by most of the free-diving fraternity as the best there is. He holds several free-diving records, including the prestigious constant weight category which involved diving to a depth of 75 metres on one lungful of air. Training at a very high level is his method.

'Free diving is a very strange discipline. Physiologically our body has a natural condition and adaptation to the depth and the pressure. For example, deeper than 100 metres, the frequency of the heartbeat decreases by 7–8 beats a minute. I dive deeper than 130 metres and at that depth the volume of the lungs is 14 times smaller than lungs at the surface.'

Doctors are baffled by Pelizzari's ability to mimic sea mammals such as dolphins, whales and seals, which on the beach have heartbeats of 300 beats a minute, yet when they dive this decreases to a third or less. For these animals, it's normal to decrease their intake of oxygen when deep under water – which is why some of them can stay down for an hour or more. According to Pelizzari, there is also the phenomenon known as 'blood shift', which is when blood leaves the extremities and fills the compressed space left empty in the lungs. 'The heart puts the blood inside this space. The blood is liquid, the liquid is incompressible, so that's why our chests don't collapse because of pressure. We have blood shifts also in dolphins, whales, all sea mammals and nobody was sure... that man could have the same phenomena. Ten, twelve years ago we tested that also man could dive deep thanks to blood shift.'

Pelizzari can hold his breath for five and a half minutes on land – yet under water this increases to over 7 minutes. He says doctors don't understand it, but he believes it's natural to us – having spent the first nine months of our lives under water. He points to the experiments in which newborn babies swim under water with pleasure even before they can crawl or sit up. He also says that he knows yogis who can hold their breath for twenty minutes.

For him, as for other free divers, there are none of the decompression problems typically experienced by scuba divers like Paul Camilli. Scuba divers' air tanks keep them supplied with air – and air causes the problems; free divers, on the other hand, have empty lungs by the time they surface.

Right Showing his remarkable lung capacity, free diver Lee Donnelly baffles doctors with his ability to dive to a depth of 50 metres on a single lungful of air. British-born Donnelly, who dives for the Israeli team, learned his breathing techniques from yoga masters in Goa.

For 'Pippin' Ferraras there was no hiding under a beach umbrella; he started his swimming and diving career as a spear-fisherman at an early age. By 1998 he made an astonishing breakthrough in breath-holding physiology by doing what had never before been accomplished: he was the first to reach the incredible free-diving depth of 152 metres (500 feet). The dive, off the island of Grand Cayman, began with a single breath at the surface and a second one at 91 metres from a spare air tank. He credits his success to 38,000 hours of training and more than 500 dives deeper than 100 metres. He has worked with physicians, scientists and marine biologists in numerous experiments focusing on aquatic medicine and mammal behaviour.

Women generally have smaller lung capacities, but can still dive to exceptional depths. Mehgan Heaney-Grier, who describes herself as a model-aquanaut, set a new US free-diving record in the constant weight category by diving 165 feet and back on a single breath.

It's not as easy as it sounds. Risks include vomiting blood, perforated eardrums, brain damage and blackouts. Pelizzari says he has never suffered from blackouts, but they are a constant danger. 'The most dangerous parts of the dive are the last ten seconds from 10 metres to the surface because that's when you burn a lot of oxygen in your body.'

So why does he risk his life in this extraordinary way?

'This is my world. I know that when I dive I can live in another world and it's like a secret, that part of the mountain that nobody's able to reach – only you.'

Free divers do have a remarkable ability but, as Jacques Piccard said, we are not fish. They have had millions of years to adapt. Without artificial aids, the undersea world is one that we can enter only briefly, as guests.

Opposite Divers at the World Free Diving Championship held in Sardinia apparently do not suffer the usual decompression problems experienced by scuba divers.

monsters of the deep

A nightmare bloodbath with hundreds of shipwrecked servicemen killed by sharks; a thousand trapped soldiers snapped up by saltwater crocodiles; legendary sea serpents and all too real giant squid; jellyfish and snails that attack with devastating venom; a deadly threat too small to see – the ocean teems with all manner of life potentially hostile to mankind, while the mysterious depths hold creatures that defy the imagination.

If we stopped to think about what savagery lurks both onshore and offshore, we would probably never set foot on a beach, let alone the ocean. However, the sea can be a wonderful playground – and it is also a place where men must go to work. One terrible event was experienced in the last days of World War II by servicemen who had come through the war unscathed, when en masse they were attacked by ferocious sharks.

Shark attack is common around the world. It is not unusual for swimmers or surfers to be attacked and killed, or have some lucky escape and live – albeit with some terrible scars – to tell the tale. But nothing could have prepared anyone for what occurred when the USS *Indianapolis* sank in the Pacific on the night of 30 July 1945.

Divers always take their lives in their hands when swimming in shark-infested seas. These divers seem unaware of the danger they are in – while the shark is only too aware of them.

THE SINKING OF THE *INDIANAPOLIS*

Launched on 7 November 1931, the 610-foot *Indianapolis* served as President Roosevelt's personal ship of state. During the war it was considered the flagship of the United States fleet, best known for delivering the world's first operational atomic bomb to the island of Tinian in the Pacific. From Tinian, the bomb was flown by the B-29 bomber, *Enola Gay*, and dropped on Hiroshima, Japan, on 6 August, bringing about an early end to the war.

After delivering the bomb on 26 July, the *Indianapolis* was ordered to join the battleship, the USS *Idaho*, at Leyte Gulf in the Philippines to prepare for the invasion of Japan. At 14 minutes past midnight on the night of 30 July, midway between Guam and Leyte Gulf, the *Indianapolis* was hit by two torpedoes fired by the Japanese submarine, the I-58. The first blew away the bow, the second struck near midship on the starboard side, close to a fuel tank and a powder magazine. The resulting explosion split the ship to the keel, knocking out all power. Within minutes she went down by the bow, rolling to starboard in the Marianas Trench – the deepest part of the Pacific, the hottest part by day, the coldest by night.

Of the 1,196 men aboard, about 900 made it into the water in the twelve minutes

before the ship sank. Few liferafts were released and most survivors wore the standard kapok lifejacket. Shark attacks began at sunrise of the first day.

Robert McGuiggan's Story

Twenty-two-year-old Robert McGuiggan was a catapult gunner's mate aboard the *Indianapolis*. He had just finished the 8–12 midnight watch and had gone back to his hammock, which he had strung up on the deck due to the stifling conditions below, when the first torpedo struck. He immediately went to his battle station where he was instructed by an officer to launch one of the ship's aircraft. He couldn't believe what he was hearing. The aircraft had no fuel and water was rising fast, with the ship listing at a 30 degree angle on the starboard side. He ignored the order and went back to his battle station. He recalls how the ship seemed empty, with most of the men already in the water. He was one of the last to leave his section of the ship. Despite

having been torpedoed twice, the ship was still moving forward at 17 knots. Robert slid down the side of the ship and jumped into the water. He felt something hit him, which stunned him for a moment. When he came up for air, he could taste oil in his mouth and felt an awful pain in his side. However, the ship was about to sink, so he swam away as fast as he could.

He was wearing a lifejacket and carried another with him which he blew up and handed to a man beside him who couldn't swim. At that moment, the cloud cover broke and the moon lit up the sea. He saw a large group of men in the distance. He turned around to see what was happening to the ship. The stern was only about 30 feet above the water and men were visibly hanging on to the fantail of the stern. As he watched, the ship and the men slid beneath the water under the moonlit sky. 'I felt that

Top 292 survivors of the USS *Indianapolis*, which was torpedoed and sunk on 30 July 1945, lined up on the deck of escort carrier the USS *Hollandia*. A further eleven men were stretcher cases after their terrible five-day ordeal in shark-infested waters. Nearly 600 men died in the tragedy.

Above As they were: Robert McGuiggan *(far left)* and Mike Kuryla *(second from right)*.

I had left my home and all my belongings. We were all out there alone with nothing. It was an empty feeling.'

As the ship sank it caused a large wave and Robert was carried towards the group of 175–200 men he had seen earlier. He was to remain with them for the next five days.

They formed a circle, tying themselves together using the straps of the lifejackets, putting the injured and those without lifejackets in the centre. Robert asked some of the men if they knew whether any of his buddies had survived, but no one knew. Many years later he would learn that he and most of the other survivors were scattered in groups over a 22-mile stretch of water, while a small group had floated off 200 miles away.

That first day, the atmosphere was fairly positive. Everyone presumed that an SOS had been sounded as the ship started to sink and that it wouldn't be long before rescue ships came to pick them up. They also knew that the *Indianapolis* was due to meet the *Idaho* the following morning for target practice, so even if an SOS had not been sent out, the *Idaho* would report them missing. The first day was spent helping the injured men and stopping others from drinking salt water. Robert recalls: 'Some of the men lost hope, especially those without lifejackets. They just swam off and never came back. We would hear screams in the distance. Some men drank salt water and they went crazy with hallucinations. They would report how they had seen the *Indianapolis* just below them and the ship contained fresh water, encouraging the others to dive down to see it; and many, in their delirious state dived, and never came up again.'

On the third day, the weather worsened with sea swells between 10 and 18 feet. Robert says the day was really bad. No one could imagine a day so bad. He continued to hear men screaming close by and at a distance but didn't at that stage know the reason why.

'At first none of us realized what was going on. At daylight we saw the sharks circling us. They kept dragging the men down. There was one man next to me and his head was forward in the water. His body was bobbing up and down and his eyes were closed. I thought he was asleep but when I pulled his head up, he was gone from the waist down. He was just a torso. We cut him out of his lifejacket and let him go.

'From then onwards I pulled my legs up and tried to hold myself in a cannonball-like position the entire time. This was very difficult, but I was conscious of the sharks circling below our group and I couldn't bear to have my legs dangling in the water. Some of the guys who had been hurt when the ship exploded were delirious. They kept breaking away from the group and dived below us in an attempt to stab the sharks with knives or other sharp objects they had on their person. They were crazy and we tried to stop them but they were very determined. They didn't know what they were doing.'

Robert and a few others led the group in prayers as the days passed. One of the most frustrating things was to hear planes roaring overhead at night, knowing that they were flying much too high to spot the men in the water. Each day the number of men would diminish. Finally, on the fourth day Robert, a trained observer, heard the roar of an aircraft and immediately knew it was an American plane. It was Wilbur Gwinn, who spotted the men in the water and sounded the alarm. Later, a sea plane piloted by Adrian Marks appeared on the scene and dropped liferafts to the men below. Robert says:

'I decided to make a move, even though I was very weak. I tried to get my lifejacket off but the knots were too tight. Luckily, I managed to slide down beneath it and then swim to the liferaft. Somehow, I found the strength. Two other guys started to follow me towards the raft. I hadn't realized just how far away that raft was. I had to swim through 18-foot swells, but made it. I grabbed hold of the cord and the raft opened. I looked around for the other two guys, but they were nowhere to be seen. Either the distance was too far for them or the sharks got them.

'I found another guy in the water and I picked him up. We took the paddles and I looked into the water for the first time and there were layers and layers of sharks. We both went berserk and started thrashing about with the paddles trying to hit them. When I had been in the water I had never looked down because the ones who did seemed to go crazy. It was as though they were hypnotized by them.'

Once in the raft, Robert felt secure, but was concerned that it would take just one bite from a shark to deflate and sink it. Putting the thought to the back of his mind, he paddled over to the group. Only fifteen men remained of the original 200 or so. They pulled them on to the raft and, exhausted, all of them slept. When he awoke, there were searchlights in the sky, circling back and forth. They started paddling towards them, but were too weak for the effort. Suddenly, a ship appeared. It was the *Talbot*. Coming alongside, it threw them a line that they hadn't the strength to catch. Marksmen on the ship started shooting in the water. The men in the raft didn't know what was happening – but it seemed that the ship had put a man in the water to swim to the raft with a rope, and they were shooting at the sharks to protect him. The planes had dropped shark repellent in the water, discolouring it as an aid in pinpointing the rafts' locations, but, according to Robert, the repellent did not work; the sharks continued to attack.

The *Talbot* picked up 23 of the 317 survivors that day. All the men were in a bad

Biting back: *anti-shark devices*

The most effective is a CO_2 dart gun developed by the US Navy. A long sharp needle is fired from a dart gun that pierces the very thick skin of a shark, releasing CO_2 gas from a cartridge into the shark's body cavity. This instantly 'blows the shark up' exactly like a balloon and it floats to the surface and dies. An electrical shark dart can stun smaller sharks. A drogue dart – a barbed lance with a parachute attached – annoys a shark so much that it supposedly forgets about the victim. An organic shark repellent that seems to work is pardaxin, a milky substance exuded by the Red Sea Moses sole and, oddly enough, fireflies. But the simplest way of avoiding sharks seems to be: make yourself invisible! Sharks cannot see through certain shades of deep red. If you spray red dye into the water, you become invisible until the dye is dispersed. Then there is a lightweight opaque bag into which a downed flier or a sailor abandoning ship can pop himself – so he looks like a jellyfish.

state. Robert could barely see because of the oil in his eyes, and he was bloated after so many days in the water. Once on board, the men were washed down with crude oil – the only way of removing the oil which covered them. They were taken to various military hospitals in the Philippines before being eventually shipped back to the US on the *Hollandia*.

Robert still thinks about what happened almost every night and, as is quite common, he feels tremendous guilt that he survived when so many didn't.

'My one big regret, and something I think about all the time, is whether there was anything I could have done to have helped the other men who didn't make it. I also think about how little we had to help us in the water. We should have had more survival gear. We had two huge whale boats on the ship, but it would have taken twenty-five minutes to launch each one and the ship went down in twelve minutes. If we had had the time, we could have got a lot of men on board and more of them would have survived.'

He still has vivid dreams and tosses and turns all night like a corkscrew. 'I can't escape the memories and I sometime relive certain parts of those memories in my dreams.'

But Robert cannot talk about some of his worst memories – not to his wife, not to his family.

Guy Kay's Story

At just eighteen Gus Kay was one of the youngest men on the *Indianapolis*. From a Greek immigrant family, he had joined when he was barely seventeen. His job on the ship was to man the 40-millimetre gun mount. The night the ship sank, he was on duty and was supposed to have been relieved at 11.45 pm, but he was told to stay at his post for a while longer since the next shift was not quite ready for duty. It is possible that those men, still below deck, never made it off the ship when it went down.

When the first torpedo hit the bow, Gus knew at once what it was. He stayed at his post until the ship started to capsize. Making it sound easy, he describes climbing over the gun mounts and simply walking down the listing hull and into the water, which was covered with burning oil. (In fact, US Navy crews were taught that they should never enter the sea by the lowest point of a sinking ship, although none seemed to know the reason why.) Gus swam underneath the slick, desperately trying to get away from the ship before it sucked him under. He could even feel the hard pull of the suction but by then was far enough away to break free.

Gus Kay *(far right)* with fellow seamen during his navy days.

It was at this point that he realized he was not wearing a lifejacket, but found a cork float net and hung on to that. He could hear men screaming. Soon he joined up with a group of over a hundred men. Shortly after, he saw a Japanese submarine which surfaced briefly and then vanished. By the second day some of the men started to drink salt water, but Gus had taken a survival course. 'I knew not to drink the water. We were also told [in the course] that if there was an oil slick, we should spread the oil on our bodies to block out the sun. It was tempting to drink the water, especially when it splashed in your face. I just put a little on my lips, that was all.'

By the fourth day every member of the group was quiet. They were just waiting to die. The situation worsened when the sharks began to stalk his group that day.

'*They stalked us for about three hours and then when they saw no real opposition they attacked the group. About sixty-three men died. I remember the turbulence of the water as the sharks thrashed about. It was terrible. I saw about twenty sharks, but there seemed to be many more than that. They were coming out of the water and grabbing at the men. People think that sharks just glide along on the surface when they are about to attack but that's not true. They seemed to come from underneath… and as they attacked they would thrust the men out of the water. I'll never forget the cries, their screams. The shark attacks are my most vivid recollections. You ask yourself, how did the sharks get those men and not me? And you wonder whether they'll come back for you. I was extremely lucky and the whole experience gave me a complete belief in God.*

'*One shark came so close I thought it was coming for me, but it took another man floating next to me. It raised him right out of the water and then another took a man on the other side of me. The sharks must have been between 15 and 20 feet long. They were huge. None of the men in my group survived the shark attacks. At night the waves would hit you and I'd think, "Jesus Christ!" – what with the sharks and the oil and then the waves, it was too much to bear.*

'*At night I'd tie myself to the floater net to stop myself drifting away, although it seemed that I didn't sleep for the five days I was in the water. Then in the morning, I'd go around with a few of the other men and check who was dead and who was alive.*'

The lifejackets were designed to last only seventy-two hours in the water; as the days wore on, they needed more and more buoyancy. So when the surviving men found a dead body they would remove his lifejacket and wear two or more just to keep afloat. It was a desperate situation, but Gus thinks he survived because he was a young man and had so much to live for. One of the worst moments for him was when his friend died shortly after Wilbur Gwinn and Adrian Marks spotted the men in the water and dropped shark repellent into the sea.

'The planes dropped this orange chemical into the water. Me and my friend, Pepe Costello, were in that area. It seemed to work as no more sharks came close, but then Pepe told me he had all the food and water he needed. I asked him if he had been drinking the water and he started to swim away from the shark repellent. Of course, the sharks got him.

'They didn't look for us at all. It was only when Gwinn flew overhead that we were spotted. We'd almost had it by the time we were picked up. Only seven men remained from our original number of about 123. When the alarm was sounded, they should have sent more sea planes. The ships took too long to arrive and a lot of men died while waiting to be rescued that final day.'

Michael Kuryla's Story

Mike Kuryla had joined the *Indianapolis* in 1943 when he was seventeen years old, working his way up to a third-class petty officer within two years. He worked alongside Robert McGuiggan. The night of the disaster, he had just finished his shift and had

Gus Kay, Mike Kuryla and Robert McGuiggan as they are today (seen here at the dedication of the USS Tranquility Hospital at Great Lakes, Canada).

gone below to the dining room. He picked up a mug of coffee and went topside to the aircraft hangar deck, where it was cooler. The ship had been zigzagging as was usual in enemy seas during his watch, but as he came off shift, Captain MacVay gave orders to the bridge to cease zigzagging and to inform him if the weather changed and the moon came out. It was a very dark and cloudy night: 'A peekaboo night, so dark you couldn't see your hand in front of you. Then the moon would come out momentarily and the whole sky would light up. It was like turning a light switch on and off.'

Mike took his shoes off and lay down on the deck. A few minutes later the first torpedo struck the ship's bow, 'like hitting a metal plate with a metal baseball bat'. He was flung into the air and as he landed back on the deck he looked towards the bow of the ship and could see flames, right where his battle station was. He went immediately to one of the gun mounts, not knowing what had happened. He wasn't sure whether the ship had been hit by a torpedo, an aircraft – or whether the engines had blown due to the high speed the ship had made during the previous few days when they were delivering the components of the atom bomb to Tinian. As he loaded the gun, the *Indianapolis* was hit again, in the midship where the ammunition store and fuel tank were placed, and there was a huge explosion.

Mike and his fellow shipmates started to cut down canvas bags hung around the ship containing lifejackets. He handed them out and grabbed one for himself, remaining at the gun mount awaiting orders. The ship was ploughing into the sea and listing. He had presumed that all the watertight doors had been closed below deck to prevent the ship from sinking, but it was so badly damaged that water was rushing in everywhere. Even so, he believed they would survive and be towed into harbour for repair – as had happened when the *Indianapolis* had been hit by a Japanese kamikaze pilot some months before.

However, he was given the order to abandon ship. As a petty officer, Mike was in charge of the boat deck, so he was ordered to start releasing the liferafts. He was forced to cut them loose with his knife and when he looked around it seemed everyone had already got off the ship. He knew that when a ship was sinking it was better to get off the high side – not the side that was already under water. He attempted to crawl up the ship, hanging on to a line of rope. The ship started to roll over and the deck loomed high above him. He was very scared.

> '*I didn't know what to do. I was holding on tight and everything was falling into the water... as the ship rolled again I was forced down into the water and I started to think about my life. I saw the street where I lived in Chicago and I saw my mother and father and my six sisters and brother... I couldn't hold my breath any more... I must have blacked out. Somehow I must have kicked my way to the surface, or my lifejacket shot me back up because I came around just in time to see the stern of the ship disappear below the water.*'

He was in shock for a while, unable to believe that such a large ship could sink so fast. His first concern was to try to help others who were injured or who didn't have lifejackets. He also hoped that some of his friends had made it off the ship. Soon, he found himself in a group of thirty-five men with a couple of liferafts. The group grew in size the following morning when they came across others who had spent the night alone in the water. Initially, they were just elated that they had got off the ship safely, convinced that the SOS had been sounded and they would be rescued soon.

The first day, they talked about being rescued. The sun beat down and became hotter and hotter. Mike instructed the men to cut off their shirt tails to protect them from the sun. They prayed a little. Towards evening they saw the first sharks close by and splashed and shouted to scare them away. It was a very cold night and they huddled together for warmth.

The next day, the men started asking Mike questions he couldn't answer, such as when would they be rescued? There was no food on the raft, but they managed to scavenge a little from the sea: an onion covered in oil, a tin of Spam, some malt tablets and a container of crackers. With these they made sandwiches.

As each day passed, the situation grew worse. Some of the men drank sea water, grew delirious and died. Their bodies just drifted off. At night they heard the screams. Mike kept telling himself: 'You're going to be rescued, you're not going to die out here. You can't give up. When I looked up at the sky, I realized just how small and insignificant we all were, out there in the Pacific, in the middle of nowhere.'

He told the men that he was going to fire a star shell off the deck of the ship in the hope that one of the passing planes would spot it. Then he realized he wasn't on the ship – he was in the water and didn't have any star shells. His tongue dried out and started to crack, he had no saliva in his mouth and gulping was painful. His whole body felt sore with saltwater ulcers. The men became more desperate as the days wore on and some swam underwater and would come up again and tell the others that there was fresh drinking water just six feet below them. These men didn't last long. 'As each man dies, you feel sorry, but your main concern is whether you'll be next... you pray and cry for them, but then you toughen up again... It gave me an even greater respect for life. It still bothers me today that I survived and got married and I have a wonderful family. Those guys didn't have all that. It still cuts me up inside.'

As a Navy man, Mike was very angry that they weren't rescued sooner, especially as a lot of men died on that last day. The *Indianapolis* didn't have sonar, only radar, so they couldn't detect submarines. Neither were they warned that enemy submarines were operating in that area – in fact, they were lulled into a false sense of security, since they were not given their usual escort of destroyers. If they had known, they would have pushed their engines to the limit and perhaps would have outrun the torpedoes.

On the fifth day, Mike saw searchlights reflected on the clouds. Fading fast, this gave him extra strength to hang on. Shark repellent and dye was dropped from a plane, and the USS *Register* dispatched barges to pick the men out of the water. Even at the eleventh hour, sharks were still attacking and the barge that picked them up had a man in the bows shooting at the sharks.

Safe aboard ship, Mike was saying that he hoped his buddy Bob McGuiggan had made it when Bob himself walked by. The two men embraced, almost unable to believe that they had survived when so many had not. Two days later, the atom bomb was dropped on Hiroshima.

Afterwards, Mike suffered from battle fatigue and took to the bottle, using alcohol as a means of forgetting what he had seen during those five terrible days. 'When I sobered up, it was still all there. I couldn't chase away those memories for long. They always come back.'

It wasn't until the movie *Jaws* was released that he was able to talk, to confront his demons, to reflect on the horror of the sharks – and to slowly come to terms with it.

Although they heard planes many times, the planes, flying at high altitudes, couldn't see the men – possibly because they were so low in the water. Also, during the five days, some of the men had drifted up to 200 miles away from where the ship went down. The ships that eventually arrived were forced to search a huge area and so it took several days before all the survivors were found. The majority – 149 survivors – were rescued by the USS *Basset*.

Many years later when a group of the *Indianapolis* survivors went to Hawaii for the twenty-fifth anniversary of the bombing of Pearl Harbor, Mochitsura Hashimoto, the captain of the Japanese submarine which had torpedoed them, revealed that he had lost all his family when the atomic bomb was dropped on Hiroshima. When some of the survivors heard that they began to change their views about the sinking of the *Indianapolis*. They said that 'many years had passed and you've got to pay the price for what you do. They delivered the bomb which killed a lot of people – then they lost an excellent ship and many good young men lost their lives.'

The Rescue

The sharks which attacked the survivors of the *Indianapolis* seemed random in their behaviour. They took dozens of men in larger groups and perhaps no one in smaller groups. They picked off lone swimmers; but equally they could be scared off by other isolated men. It also seemed that they did not attack men in float nets.

Shortly after 11 am of the fourth day the survivors were accidentally discovered by Ventura Bomber pilot, Wilbur Gwinn, on a routine antisubmarine patrol. Radioing his base, he alerted the military to 'many men in the water'. A seaplane, piloted by Adrian Marks, was dispatched to lend assistance. En route Marks flew over the destroyer, USS *Cecil Doyle*, and alerted her captain to the emergency. The *Doyle* diverted to the scene.

Arriving hours ahead of the *Doyle*, Marks's crew began dropping rubber rafts and supplies. While doing this, many of them observed men being attacked by sharks. Horrified and disregarding orders not to land at sea, Marks landed and began taxi-ing to pick up the stragglers and lone swimmers who were at greater risk of shark attack. Learning the men were the crew of the almost legendary US flagship, the *Indianapolis*, he radioed the news, requesting immediate assistance. As darkness fell, Marks waited for help to arrive, all the while continuing to seek out and pull nearly dead men from the water. When the plane was full, survivors were tied to the wing with parachute cord. Marks and his crew rescued fifty-six men that day.

The USS *Cecil Doyle* was the first vessel on the scene and began taking survivors on board. Disregarding the safety of his own vessel against potential enemy action, the captain pointed his largest searchlight into the night sky to serve as a beacon for other rescue vessels. This beacon was the first indication to most survivors that their prayers had been answered. Help had at last arrived.

Sadly – or perhaps remarkably – a coda to this tragic story is that the captain of the *Indianapolis*, Charles MacVay, was court-martialled for not zigzagging, a standard precautionary measure against attack, used to confuse the enemy. It was the first time a captain was court-martialled for losing a ship during war time; and also the first time that the enemy was asked to give evidence against the defendant. After the war, Captain Mochitsura Hashimoto was brought in to testify that MacVay was not zigzagging when he fired the torpedoes. Part of MacVay's defence was that he was not given an escort of a Navy destroyer and so was lulled into a false sense of security in believing that his ship was considered safe from attack.

The members of the *Indianapolis* Survivors Association are still working to exonerate Captain MacVay from blame. Robert McGuiggan says: 'We have been a source of embarrassment to the Navy for years. As long as we're alive, we are their sore thumb.'

MORE MAN-EATERS

Andy Carter is one of the few men to have survived a double attack by a great white shark. June, July and August are the peak times for shark attacks off South African shores. In June 1994, Andy's left leg was bitten to the bone from hip to knee in a horrific attack that left him close to death. His friend, fellow surfer Bruce Corby, was also attacked and died from massive injuries inflicted by the same shark.

It was a glorious hot Saturday at East London's famous Nahoon Reef, a mecca for surfers, even though it doesn't have an anti-shark net. Andy, one of South Africa's top

Andy Carter feels lucky to have survived a horrific double attack by a great white shark off South Africa in 1994. He still bears terrible scars and shows here the chunk bitten out of the surfboard that he wedged in the shark's jaws, ultimately saving his life.

professional surfers, was lying face down on his board, paddling hard 200 metres offshore, when he was hit from nowhere by the most powerful force he had ever felt. An hour before, he had felt something big underneath him, but assumed it was a rock.

'There was a fabulous clear blue sky and I'd been out surfing for a while. Suddenly, I felt this huge bang from behind. I realized straight away it was a shark. The first three seconds were the worst.'

Pinned to his surfboard, Andy twisted his neck and looked over his shoulder. 'I saw a big, black shiny head. Its teeth were embedded in my thigh and board. I remember its power. It was the most helpless feeling. It had its jaws clamped around my leg and my board, pulling me down into the water. I felt like my bones would snap. It was like being in a massive vice. Its jaws must have been four or five feet long.'

Andy felt the shark biting him, but he didn't feel much pain because of the adrenaline surge. He felt only a crushing sensation and a fear of dying because he was so far offshore, totally helpless in the shark's domain. The other surfers heard Andy's piercing scream and later said that it seemed as though the shark was biting him in half because its jaw was right over his leg and the water all around him was completely red. As soon as they saw what was happening, most of the other surfers turned around and paddled not towards Andy – but straight for shore. Andy says: 'Everyone knows you can't help someone escape from a shark that size.'

Andy firmly gripped his board when suddenly the shark opened its mouth to get a bigger bite. It went back into the water and lunged forward again. Andy was holding his board so tightly it somehow twisted round and jammed in the shark's mouth, giving him a moment's grace to swim away.

'I kept looking back because I was terrified it would come at me from behind. Then I saw it let go of the board and disappear. That was the scariest point, swimming to shore and not being able to see where its next attack would come from. But I was too far from shore and losing an enormous amount of blood, moments away from passing out. In

desperation, I clawed my way back on to my surfboard and as I grabbed it,
I caught the luckiest wave of my life, which carried me in to shore.'

Andy made it to a rock next to the beach and crawled on top. He saw his blood streaming away from him and realized he had to stay absolutely still to prevent further blood loss. He tried to stop the flow by pressing down on his thigh; when his hand disappeared inside his leg, he thought, 'That shark has bitten my backside!'

He got two girls sunbathing on the beach to come to his aid. They packed their clothes into the massive wound and bound up his leg. It was then that the realization of what had happened hit home and he suffered from the effects of extreme shock. He started to see his life flowing past him. His vision went and he could hardly hear, but realized he had no fear of death.

But for fellow surfer, 22-year-old Bruce Corby, there had been no lucky escape. Thwarted of one victim, the shark went after another. Bruce had been further out when Andy was attacked and the slowest to react. Everyone else headed straight for the shore at top speed. None of them saw the shark turn on Bruce, and no one realized that he had been attacked until he got out of the water. Another surfer, John Borne, saw Bruce coming in on a wave and shouted to him to get out of the water as Andy had been attacked and told him to come and help Andy. Almost casually, Bruce told him he had been attacked too. He seemed so normal that at first John thought he was joking.

When Bruce got out of the water, everyone was appalled to see that his right leg had actually been severed at the knee by the great white. His injury was severe, though survivable with prompt medical aid – but Bruce went into shock and within two minutes stopped breathing. They gave him artificial respiration on the beach and revived him – but he was already brain dead and died forty-eight hours later.

Andy underwent five hours of surgery; over 400 stitches were needed to sew each tendon and muscle on his thigh and buttock back together. In hospital, he had many nightmares of sharks coming into his room and attacking him. For months, he was unable to sleep without a light. He was not told of Bruce Corby's death until several days after the attack, and it was that which brought home how close to death he himself had been. Corby's parents came to visit him in the hospital and, like many people who escape when a friend does not, he felt deeply guilty that he was the one to survive.

A year after the attack, Andy went back to the same spot to surf; but he began to panic and made a speedy return to shore. He was also keen to find out as much as he could about sharks.

'I wasn't taken in by all that rubbish scientists talk about the shark not
meaning to attack me but simply taking an exploratory bite. That great
white went straight for Bruce. It took him right off the top of his board. It
didn't even get to touch the board. That shark was definitely out to eat one
or both of us. It didn't get me, so it went after Bruce.
'I don't like sharks but I know they've got a reason to be in the ocean and

I haven't really. I wouldn't go and walk around in a cage of lions, but I'm prepared to swim in an ocean where there are things that can kill you. I'm so used to the sea – I've been surfing for twenty-six years (since the age of nine) – that I accept the dangers. That's my choice.'

Andy still experiences panic attacks when he is in the water and often heads quickly back to shore. Before the attack, he used to surf alone in remote locations but now he takes more care and goes where there are plenty of people in the water because sharks don't usually like people in groups, preferring to attack the solitary swimmer. But only the day before this interview, he had been chased out of the water by a shark. He sees about a dozen sharks a year and admits he still takes risks, such as staying out until nightfall – a dangerous time because most sharks feed nocturnally. He stayed out because the waves were so good.

Twenty-nine-year-old Martin Richardson was on a diving course in the Red Sea in 1996 when he had a near-fatal encounter with a shark. At the end of a day's tuition, he had been playing around with a school of dolphins, when they suddenly disappeared. He decided to tread water where he was and enjoy the silence of the sea and the desert while waiting for the launch to come out to pick him up. Out of the blue, he felt something rip into his back. When he saw blood billowing up all around him, he knew he had been attacked by a shark. The shark – probably an oceanic white tip – came back for another huge bite out of his back, then turned and tried to take off the shoulder and arm Martin had tried to use in self-defence. Just when he thought the end was near, he noticed that the dolphins had returned – and the shark had gone.

David George, of the Marine Biological Services Division at London's Natural History Museum, says: 'Dolphins regard sharks as enemies and can drive them off – even kill them by ramming them with their beak-like snouts. There have been numerous instances of dolphins apparently trying to help people in danger, such as holding a drowning person above water.'

Martin was severely wounded; he required some 300 stitches, and had lost at least 20 per cent of his blood.

Opposite A grey reef shark showing its ferocious jaws as it prowls the seas looking towards the surface for a potential meal. According to many experts, sharks don't really intend attacking humans – they mistake them for their usual diet of seals or sea lions. But those who have been attacked are not convinced that this is the case.

Kenny Doudt felt he should have seen all the warning signs – schools of small fish breaking the surface of the sea off Cannon Beach, Oregon, not to mention two surfers rapidly leaving the water. They shouted something, but were too far away to be properly heard and, anxious to take advantage of the good surfing conditions, Kenny was already heading for the water. Perhaps the warning he should have taken the most notice of was the warning of two local fishermen who had seen a large white attack a sealion a few miles down the coast, tossing it into the air like a toy before devouring it.

But Kenny ignored all these warnings and went into the water, unaware that one of nature's greatest predators was cruising just below the surface, mere yards away.

At first, Kenny thought he was being hit by a sealion, common in that area. The sound he had heard before the great pressure was a muffled roar. Then above him, he

saw a giant shark rise up out of the water, jaws agape.

The great jaws clamped down on him and his surfboard, pulling him underwater. He was released, then grabbed and dragged under for the second time. While Kenny screamed for help the shark grabbed him for the third time, shaking him in the air like a dog with a rat.

Suddenly, Kenny was released. The shark had vanished.

Kenny's chewed-up body was held together only by his shredded wet suit. Without it, all his vital organs would be exposed. Nerves and blood vessels and muscles were sliced in half. The surgical team at St Vincent's Hospital, Portland, gave up counting the stitches when they got to 500 – possibly a record after a shark attack.

But why had the shark gone when it could have eaten Kenny as easily as it had swallowed the sealion? According to many shark experts, sharks don't really want to eat humans but they often mistake them for their natural food. Someone in a sleek black wet suit can look like a seal; on a surfboard with four limbs gently paddling through the water they can resemble a giant turtle with a shell and flippers from a shark's eye view. They cannot define colour – just shape.

Those who have been attacked by sharks don't always agree with that. As Andy Carter said of the great white that attacked him. 'That shark knew exactly what he was doing.'

CROC!

Sharks are well known for attacking humans; less well known is the saltwater crocodile. However, while nearly 600 American servicemen from the *Indianapolis* were killed by sharks, just some months earlier nearly 1,000 Japanese soldiers had been

killed and eaten by the giant saltwater crocodile. This monster, the most deadly of the crocodiles and anything from 20 to 33 feet long, is responsible for the largest mass-killing of human beings by any other animal recorded in history. The tale is well recorded by naturalist Bruce Wright, who was there when the mass killing took place and told the story in his book, *Wildlife Sketches, Near and Far*.

The terrible event occurred during World War II, on 19–20 February 1945 in a mangrove swamp on the Burma shore. Some 1,000 Japanese soldiers, many of them badly wounded, had

A saltwater crocodile, its belly full, rests on the bank of a lagoon while it digests its prey. It was creatures like this that killed and ate nearly 1,000 Japanese servicemen trapped in salt marshes during World War II.

been trapped by British troops at the edge of a mangrove swamp on Ramree Island. The Japanese tried to escape the blockade by breaking through the swamp, which consists of miles of waist-high water and ooze. It is doubtful if either the British or the Japanese were aware of the fact that the swamp was home to thousands of saltwater crocodiles.

Wright describes it: 'The din of the British barrage had caused all the crocodiles within miles to slide into the water and lie with only their eyes above, watchfully alert. When it subsided, the ebbing tide brought to them, more strongly and in greater volume than they had ever known it before, the scent and taste that aroused them as nothing else could – the smell of blood. Silently, each snout turned into the current, and the great tails began to weave from side to side.'

When the tide fell, the crocodiles moved in on the mired Japanese troops and began attacking. Wright reported that the sound of their thrashing and the screams of their victims were heard by the British outside the swamp. At the end of the dreadful night, only twenty Japanese soldiers had survived. Some had been killed by British gunfire and others drowned, but it is estimated that 900 men died in the jaws of the saltwater crocodiles.

It is said that the legend of St George and the Dragon was based on a Crusader who slew 'a sea dragon' that was terrorizing the people near Antioch. The beast had a jawbone as big as a horse's and it was nailed above the town gates. It was seen by travellers up until the end of the last century, who said it was probably that of a giant saltwater crocodile. It is no longer there – one night it mysteriously disappeared. The Maoris of New Zealand also have what could be a man-eating crocodile in their legends. They call it the taniwha, a monster which took the form of a lizard, snake or fish. It lived everywhere, in springs, rivers, caves, lakes and mountains. With supernatural powers, it could fly through the air and transform itself into other creatures. The origins of the legends are obscure but it has been suggested that the taniwha represents some folk-memory of the man-eating crocodiles of the Western Pacific region. There, the name for crocodile is moko-tolo; and the Maori uses the same word, moko, for all lizards and for the taniwha.

St George tilting at a dragon. But was the dragon really a giant salt-water crocodile? Many legends in the Middle East suggest that it could have been, and that St George was a Crusader who saved a town from the marauding beast.

The incredible water-spouting 'Great Sea Serpent, Pontoppidan' – drawn from contemporary descriptions of its many sightings in 1755 off Norway.

FABLED GIANTS

We have explored less than one per cent of the ocean; the far side of the moon is more familiar to us. Because there have been so few human visitors to the black depth of the deep sea, scientists have had to rely on trawled specimens, photographs taken by robotic cameras or, occasionally, observations from deep-diving submersibles, to get even the vaguest idea of what's down there. Imagine how little would be known of the rain forest if we had lowered a few baskets at random from the sky and hoped that something interesting would drop into them, and then stay put while we hauled it up – say, the odd howler monkey or harpy eagle.

Water being 800 times more buoyant than air, marine creatures are less affected by gravity than their terrestrial cousins, and so they are free to assume weird and wonderful shapes – and it is those shapes that both terrify and delight us.

In the fourth century BC Aristotle wrote of large serpents off Libya: 'Mariners sailing along the coast have told how they have seen the bones of many oxen which, it was apparent to them, had been devoured by the serpents. And as their ships sailed on, the serpents came to attack them, some of them throwing themselves on a trireme and capsizing it.'

In 1554 the Archbishop of Uppsala in Sweden, Olaus Magnus, described a sea serpent measuring 200 feet long and 20 feet thick. It had hair hanging from its neck and sharp scales; while in 1734 another Norwegian, a missionary called Hans Egede, wrote of a 'terrible sea monster' he saw off Greenland. 'It had a long, sharp snout, and blew like a whale, had broad, large flippers and the body, as it were, covered with a hard skin, and it was very wrinkled and uneven on its skin; moreover, on the lower part it was formed like a snake, and when it went under the water again, it cast itself backwards, and in doing so it raised its tail above the water, a whole ship-length from its body. That evening we had very bad weather.'

British reports of sea serpents in the nineteenth century were centred on 'the animal of Stronsa' in the Orkneys, which was washed up on shore after a storm in 1808. The carcass of a monster was seen by fifty fishermen and local people, and experts inspected the body. It was described as being some 55 feet long with a mane of hair running down the full length of the back, a tiny head and a long neck. Opinion was divided: some said it was unknown, others that the remains were those of a basking shark.

Today among the other exotic exhibits in the Royal Scottish Museum in Edinburgh is a piece of the backbone of the Stronsa beast. After seeing a rotting basking shark in December 1977, which was stranded on the shore of the Tay near Carnoustie, the curator came to the conclusion that the same description fitted both animals.

But a rotting basking shark certainly doesn't explain the recently dead beast with great teeth – a basking shark's are tiny – which came ashore at Gourock on the River Clyde in 1942. Unfortunately, because the taking of photographs were not permitted in that militarily sensitive area at the time, none were taken. No one quite knew what to do with the dead creature – but one thing was certain: soon it would rot and stink the town out. So on the orders of the borough surveyor, Charles Rankin, it was taken away, chopped up and buried under what is now the football pitch of St Ninian's RC primary school, Gourock. Rankin recalls that the animal was about 28 feet long, whole and not rotting, so he had a good look at it. He says it was nothing like a shark nor anything else he had ever seen.

It wasn't until 1938, when fishermen in the Indian Ocean off East Africa brought up a metallic-blue fish almost 6 feet long with large, thick scales and strong fleshy fins, that it was realized the sea still has many secrets. The strange fish was spotted by Dr Marjorie Courtenay-Latimer, then curator of the East London Museum. Although she did not know what it was, she realized it was quite exceptional, so she sent a rough sketch of the creature to Professor J. L. B. Smith, an eminent amateur fish expert at Rhodes University in the United States. Describing himself as almost overcome with excitement, he identified it as a coelacanth, which is now called *Latimeria chalumnae* in Dr Courtenay-Latimer's honour.

Professor Smith commented: 'My surprise would have been little greater if I had

A prehistoric sea monster come to life. The coelacanth – a fish known to have existed some 400 million years ago – was thought to have been long extinct and existing just as a fossil, until one was dredged up by fishermen off the coast of Africa in 1938. And if such a creature can still exist, what else might be lurking undiscovered in the depths of the oceans?

seen a dinosaur walking down the street' – for the fish had been known only as a fossil in rocks 400 million years old: 200 million years older than the dinosaurs. With hearts more primitive than those of any other vertebrate, and brains only one-fifteen-thousandth of their body weight, they belong to an era when the world was young. It had been thought that only a few hundred remain, living at depths of 500–1,000 feet near the Comoros islands between Madagascar and Mozambique. Recently, though, there has been further evidence that the seas hold many secrets. In the summer of 1998, other specimens of coelacanth were found among the coral reefs of Indonesia, 6,000 miles away. How had they avoided detection for so long?

The fact is, this 'extinct' fish was caught when scientists said it was absolutely impossible. And without the crucial evidence of a body, they still would be saying, 'They don't exist, they're extinct.' What else is down there in the vast reaches of the sea that scientists deny the existence of?

Take the fur seal. Their diet seems to consist of an unknown species of fish, a fact that is highly significant when contemplating the sparseness of our knowledge about the life of the ocean. Fur seals' stomachs have yielded the bones of a species of fish that has never been seen alive. Indeed, not even its remains have been found anywhere except in the stomachs of seals. Ichthyologists say this 'seal fish' belongs to a group that typically inhabits very deep water, off the edge of the continental shelf of the western United States. And surely 4 million seals could not compete with commercial fishermen for the same fish without the fact being known – so how deep do they go and where do they feed?

In the Belly of the Beast

Sharks are renowned for swallowing all kinds of weird and wonderful objects, such as . . . the body of a headless knight in full armour; a soldier in full military dress; an entire horse; a buffalo; a reindeer. Then there was the shark that thought it was Noah's Ark: in its stomach was found another shark, along with a goat, a turtle, a cat and three birds. Other unusual snacks have included nine pairs of shoes; tin cans; wood and rope; tyres; bits of cars; numerous items of clothing (presumably they were adorning people at the time); a full-grown spaniel; a yellow-billed cockatoo; six hens and a rooster; bottles of beer; a barrel of ale; a handbag; and twenty-five bottles of Vichy water . . .

Some meals have lived to tell the tale – at least one has, a Victorian Jonah. In February 1891 a British whaler, 21-year-old James Bartley, was swallowed by an 80-foot sperm whale, and survived after two days in the 104-degree heat of its belly. While harpooning the whale, Bartley was hit by its tail; he and his boat flew in the air and Bartley slithered, feet first, down the whale's throat. The next day, the 100-ton harpooned whale died from its injuries and floated on the surface of the sea. When the whale's stomach was cut open, along with thousands of shrimps Bartley shot out. Miraculously, he was alive, although his skin was bleached white in patches. For the rest of his life he was terrified of the dark – and of the sea.

We have to be careful not to confuse superstition with fact. Early Mediterranean peoples believed that fossilized sharks' teeth were snakes' tongues turned to stone. When St Paul visited Malta in AD 60 he was shown some. But it is possible that the teeth St Paul saw and remarked upon were in fact the teeth of a huge extinct shark, Megalodon, which could have been 100 feet long.

No one is suggesting that Megalodon still exists – but the fact is, we simply don't know. Another creature with giant jaws, a shark known as megamouth, the most mysterious of all sharks, was accidentally dredged up from deep water by the US Navy as recently as 1976. It can be 16 feet long and weigh almost a ton. But, despite its huge mouth and ferocious appearance, it is harmless to man; with its tiny teeth it eats only small creatures.

It's not such a vast leap from coelacanth to megamouth to sea serpent. Can sea serpents exist? If the numerous sightings are anything to go by, the answer is yes, they can. However, no one has actually produced one, alive or dead for inspection – or even taken a photograph. But dozens of captains have recorded such sightings in their ships' logs and no skipper makes an entry in his log without a very good reason.

The earliest legendary sea serpents were the kraken, or Norwegian sea-dragon, the biggest of the giant sea monsters. Many stories abound in Norway's literature of fishermen who have been terrorized by this appearing and disappearing leviathan; with its bumpy spine and tentacles floating like strands of seaweed, it was often mistaken for a good-sized island.

The strange creature known as the Gloucester Sea Serpent was observed by hundreds of witnesses lazily swimming off Cape Ann near Gloucester, Massachusetts, for two weeks in the August of 1817. After it was first sighted, the news spread like wildfire and people flocked to the point to watch its antics as it cruised back and forth on the tranquil surface of the sea for an hour or more at any one time.

As news spread far and wide, scientists from the Boston Society of Naturalists descended on Gloucester to study the serpent, getting within 100 yards of it. In fact, in the name of science, one of them, Solomon Allen, shot at it and missed. Again in the name of science – since the creature showed no interest in harming anyone – Captain Joseph Woodward, skipper of a schooner, the *Adamant*, fired a cannonball at it. The ball just bounced off.

A worthy committee appointed by New England's Linnean Society put a series of questions independently to eight reliable witnesses and, after studying their answers, came to the conclusion that this monster really did exist. It was described as being dark brown with the head of a turtle or rattlesnake, 50–100 feet long, as thick as 'half a barrel', and it had 'bunches of bumps' scattered over its back. When it moved, it held its head about a foot out of the water, twisting and turning as it travelled at about 30 miles an hour. It submerged like a stone rather than diving down.

The committee wrote in their report: 'We consider the foregoing testimony sufficient to place the existence of the animal without a doubt.' And no doubt they would have wanted to study it some more – talk was afoot of netting it – but obviously the canny creature had had enough of bullets and cannonballs; after two weeks of being the star attraction offshore that summer, the Gloucester Sea Serpent disappeared as suddenly as it had appeared.

Could it – and all the other sea serpents described down the years, often by reliable witnesses – have been the plesiosaur? The descriptions are remarkably similar. Like the coelacanth, the plesiosaur was considered to be extinct – in its case, 100 million years ago. Fossils have shown it to be a long-necked, small-headed reptile that lived in the sea. Because its nostrils were set near the top of its head, it rarely had to surface fully to breathe – and if it still existed today this would perhaps explain why it is so rarely seen. The largest one, *Kronosaurus queenlandicus*, swam in seas around Australia, attaining a length of 55 feet, the largest marine reptile ever recorded. The drawback to this theory is that, like a turtle, the plesiosaur came on shore to lay its eggs. But it is possible that over the course of 100 million years the plesiosaur has

An illustration based on an actual sighting by round-the-world sailor, Frank Bullen, of a fight between a sperm whale and a giant squid, published in his best-selling book, *The Cruise of the Albatross.*

evolved to giving birth to live young, as do some sharks and snakes. It's a fascinating theory but, unless a live one is found – as in the case of the coelacanth – it will remain pure speculation.

'Sea serpents' are still being spotted in more recent times. In 1976 just 30 miles off the Lizard in Cornwall, two fishermen, George Vinnicombe and John Cox, reported that they were 25–30 miles offshore when they saw what they took to be another boat on the horizon. When they got closer they could see it wasn't an upturned boat, but something that stunned them. Dark in colour with humps on the back, it was a creature as long as their ship – 32 feet – weighing about two tons and rising about 3 feet out of the water. After a few minutes it gradually sank in the water and disappeared. Both men were convinced that it could be nothing else but 'a prehistoric animal'.

Many scientists believe that so-called sea serpents are actually giant squid – and certainly proof exists that squid of massive proportions really do exist. An actual specimen of the 32-foot tentacle of a squid that attacked a rowing boat over 150 years ago may still be seen today, pickled in formaldehyde. In 1873 three fishermen – Daniel Squires, Theophibes Picot and Picot's 12-year-old son, Tom – were fishing off Newfoundland when they saw a large shape drifting by. At first they thought it was the upturned hull of another boat and prodded it with the boathook. Much to their terror, the huge object exploded upwards through the water and turned into an infuriated monster that seized the boat with its tentacles. The two men froze with fear – but young Tom seized an axe and chopped off a tentacle. The squid let go and vanished, leaving the great length of its tentacle quivering in the bottom of the boat. On their return to harbour, the three fishermen were treated as intrepid heroes, especially young Tom. But at least it proved to the sceptical that, if not sea serpents, then at least giant squid existed.

Naval officer Lieutenant R. E. Cox's shipmate was not so lucky. Cox was returning home to England in 1942 when his troopship was sunk by a German raider in the South Atlantic. Cox found himself on a fragile raft with twelve companions, beset by sharks. On the evening of the fifth day, by which time half the men had perished, came a sinister assault. An enormous shape appeared beside the raft and a huge arm came over and snatched one of the men and tore him off the raft before the others could do anything to save him. Then another arm, or tentacle, came over the side of the raft. Cox clearly saw it silhouetted against the starlit sky. It fastened itself on him, round his right leg and round his body. Cox's companions, weak as they were, grabbed on and held him – and instead of him being pulled over the sides, the suckers pulled the skin off his body. On his return, Cox showed the evidence to a friend, biologist Professor Cloudsley Thompson. All up his leg were deep white scars the size of a penny where the skin had been pulled off by the squid's suckers.

More recently, the USS frigate *Stein* had to return to San Diego harbour because something at sea had assaulted the anti-submarine sonar dome cover, ripping it and rendering it unserviceable. Embedded in the cover were hard bony objects several inches long that resembled large claws or teeth, later identified as the rasping tools set into the suction discs of a giant squid's tentacles. Navy biologist F. G. Woods has a sample of the cover, but the 'teeth' have been lost. Woods says: 'It's apparent that whatever did this damage grasped the dome and ripped all the way through this rubber covering to the metal below.'

An imaginary scene from Jules Verne's *20,000 Leagues Under the Sea*, showing a ship's crew attacking a giant squid with harpoons and guns. Until recently such creatures were thought to be pure invention – but confirmed sightings and even a few specimens washed up on beaches have proved that they really do exist.

The giant squid's mortal enemy is the sperm whale, which grows up to 60 feet in length, weighing around 70 tons. Sperm whales live in groups of up to 30 females and calves, protected by a single large male. Able to dive down to 1,500 feet or more beneath the surface, they can stay underwater for over an hour, where they hunt giant squid using echo-location by producing sounds and listening for the echo to bounce off their prey. The ferocious combat of these leviathans, which often takes them to the surface, could look like the twinings of a snake-like creature. The head of the sperm whale is often marked with long stripes, which consist of a great number of circular scars made by the suckers of the squid.

Until recently, all reported sightings of the squid have been on the surface of the sea, for submarines have no observation windows (despite Captain Nemo's fantastic vessel in *20,000 Leagues Under The Sea*) and the bottom of the ocean is scarcely our usual habitat. However, oceanographer Richard Ellis describes in *Deep Atlantic* his encounter with a giant squid, probably the only authenticated undersea observation of the squid in its natural habitat. Ellis was the first person to travel underwater from New York to Sagres in Portugal, where Atlantic exploration began. He was in the specially built submersible, *Navegador*, past the Azores, some 300 miles from his destination, when the momentous meeting occurred. The legend became reality, eclipsing imagination: 'For a brief, spectacular moment, we were vouchsafed a sight that no humans before us had ever experienced: we have seen the living *Architeuthis*.'

It's possible that some sightings or attacks attributed to squid are in fact due to octopus. Most scientists agree that octopus are shy, retiring creatures, but reports

suggest otherwise. Octopus secrete a neurotoxin that can be quite harmful to humans – usually, the result of an octopus attack is severe pain and a wound that heals slowly – but there have been rare cases of death from octopus poisoning. However, octopus will fight interlopers to the death over territory and there have been cases of giant specimens attacking ships and divers. In 1874 Captain Floyd, master of a 150-ton schooner, *Pearl*, reported in a London newspaper that his ship had been wrecked and two of his crew killed when a giant octopus attacked it. 'We were all looking over the side at the advancing monster. We could see now a large oblong mass... just under the surface of the water... its wake or train was 100 feet long... the brute struck us and the ship quivered under its thud; in another moment, monstrous arms like trees seized the vessel and she reeled over and in another moment the monster was aboard, squeezed in between the masts.'

More recently an octopus washed up on the beach at St Augustine, Florida, was the largest specimen ever found. Its arms measured 100 feet and, according to Dr Joseph F. Gennaro Jr who identified it, 'from the tip of one tentacle to the tip of an opposing one it could have stretched across 200 feet of ocean'. Its remains alone weighed more than six tons.

Another sea creature that doesn't live up to its reputation – and this time it's not as dangerous as popularly supposed – is the manta ray; called devil fish because of its strange 'horns', it has also been mistaken for a sea monster. Until the 1920s the manta was thought to be a dangerous predator, but divers now swim safely with these giants. Despite its huge size, it is harmless and feeds only on floating plankton. The horns simply direct plankton-rich water into its mouth. However, by accident they have landed on small craft and even sunk them. Only recently was it known that these leaps are part of one of the strangest of rituals. Both the manta ray and the spotted ray leap out of the water to give birth while airborne. Their young are ejected, spread their pectoral fins and descend to the sea like parachutes.

Since almost 40 per cent of the Earth's surface lies under water masses that are from 2 to 3 miles deep, vast regions where no one has ever been, dark impenetrable regions which can scarcely be explored except with the aid of lights, anything is possible.

Pure Venom

Sharks undoubtedly have earned the title 'most dangerous' since they are the most visible and their attacks the most frequently reported. But there are many other marine creatures which are equally as dangerous, in other ways. After all, you're just as dead if eaten by a shark, stung by a deadly jellyfish or bitten by a venomous yellow-bellied sea snake. You can die within minutes if bitten by a tiny blue-ringed Pacific octopus – a venom which has no known antidote – or after you've tucked into a gourmet meal of shark's liver (the oil, when used in cosmetics, is safe) or play a deadly game of epicurean Russian roulette with a sliver of raw blowfish, as many Japanese do.

The people who are most affected by fatal confrontations with venomous sea creatures are not always, as might be supposed, the professionals who work in and around the sea, but the unwary holiday-maker. In Australia, school children are warned about the dangers of the blue-ringed octopus, one of the deadliest animals found in the sea. But to a tourist, the beautifully marked little creature is so small and shy it seems harmless when found on the shore, hiding in a polystyrene cup or a Coke can, or inside the smallest crack of a rock a child might turn over while looking for crabs. As its name suggests, the blue-ringed octopus is covered with azure blue circles that get

Above The tiny blue-ringed octopus of the Pacific is one of the most dangerous creatures known to man, killing within minutes, using a venom that has no known antidote.

Left Carefree holiday-makers – but they never know what's lurking, not just out in the ocean where they're swimming, but also on the beach where they're walking with bare feet.

bluer when it is aroused. Barely half an inch across, even with tentacles spread, it reaches no more than four inches, injecting its venom through its horny beak. And once bitten, there is no point in running for help, even supposing there were an antidote: victims are dead in a couple of minutes. A rare bacterium living inside its mouth produces a neurotoxin that helps subdue its prey in seconds and in humans it causes fatal paralysis and suffocation. Many people presumed drowned are believed to have been victims of the blue-ringed octopus.

Most poisonous of all sea creatures is the sea wasp, a small jellyfish, a Cherybderd, member of the box jelly group. 'It was as if someone had tied electric wire around my wrist and switched on the current,' reported one diver who survived. The sea wasp looks harmless enough. It is a small box-shaped transparent blob found mainly in the Indo-Pacific area, especially off Australian beaches. But it packs a sting of death with a venom so potent it can kill within half a minute from the touch of its dangling tentacles. Its poison enters the blood stream, attacks the nervous system, can cause a victim to break into a fierce sweat, go blind, gasp for breath and die, almost immediately, because its chief effect is to paralyse the heart.

In fact, its toxin is so deadly that even when diluted 10,000 times in water, it causes death in laboratory animals even before the hypodermic can be removed. There are more signs warning against the sea wasp on Australian beaches than there are signs warning against sharks. And although it is so warm in the sea, divers wear wet suits as a precaution against the sea wasp. In fact, this creature is far more poisonous than any other animal on Earth, claiming on average fifty known victims a year. The personal surgery score, kept by one Brisbane doctor, is: sharks 13; sea wasps 60.

While not as venomous as the sea wasp, many other jellyfish can also inflict fatal stings – even when they're dead, so when they're washed up on a beach they should never be touched. The poisons of certain jellyfish are exceptionally virulent. The stinging cells of the strong-swimming Charybderds, for instance, have inflicted fatal injuries to humans. Such stinging cells, or nematocysts, are unique, being found nowhere else in the animal kingdom.

The best known among the poisonous long-tentacled jellyfish is *Physalia pelagica*, or the Portuguese man-o'-war, native to all tropical waters – even though they are sometimes found drifting close to land or washed ashore in colder regions, like Britain or the northern United States. Small as it is, *Physalia* can be deadly. Actually not an individual animal but a colony of highly specialized polyps, it has tentacles up to

Named a Portuguese man-o'-war because of its distinctive billowing 'sail', this jellyfish is dangerous. Its tentacles – often 50-feet long – discharge toxins which can paralyse or even kill swimmers.

50 feet long which discharge a toxic substance that has painfully stunned, paralysed and even killed swimmers coming into contact with it.

There are at least fifty species of sea snakes harmful to humans; and many are more venomous than their land cousins, possessing venom fifty times more lethal than the king cobra. Their bite is not generally painful – sometimes hardly felt – but the symptoms can develop within twenty-four hours and probably 25 per cent of all people bitten die. Sea snakes are found everywhere, except in the Atlantic, the Mediterranean and the Red Sea. They are true snakes but can remain submerged for hours without surfacing for air because they have no lungs. The types that have caused death include the 5-foot yellow sea snake found in deep water; the potent 3-foot beaked sea snake of shallow Asian waters; the 2-foot yellow-bellied pelagic sea snake that often floats on the surface of South American waters; the 4-foot annulated sea snake which ranges from mangrove swamps to the sea; and Hardwicke's sea snake, a 2-foot yellowish snake that lives off the Philippines. Oddly, only eagles and some humans will eat sea snakes – all other creatures avoid them.

The cone shell is said to be one of the most beautiful and desirable shells in the world to a collector. It is also deadly. Many shells feed on algae or carrion but the cone is a predator, travelling over the sea bed on its large fleshy foot. It has a long feeler armed with poisonous darts that it uses to paralyse small fish and worms – the only snail poisonous enough to kill a human. The neurotoxin is delivered on little hollow harpoons or tongues in its mouth that pass through its nose (its other name is 'poison-tongued'). These ever-ready harpoons deliver a poison related to curare and are left stuck in victims while, incredibly, the animal quickly replaces each one from a pouch near its head.

The deadly crown of thorns starfish, close relative of the common starfish, has killed a number of people; but far more dangerous to the environment than its poisonous spines is its voracious appetite. Known as 'the gangster of the deep with a bullet-proof vest', it is threatening to destroy the entire Great Barrier Reef, eating its way at a rate that could kill it all within a few years. It has already destroyed several other reefs, devouring everything as it marches onward in plague proportions. Nothing seems to destroy it. Cutting them up merely serves to produce more – any part of the whole seems able to grow into a new starfish.

Several types of sea urchin are poisonous. The sharp spines, often up to 12 inches in length, of the long-spined black sea porcupine (Diadema) can penetrate deep into the flesh, the tips breaking off and depositing a venom that stings worse than a hornet's until they are removed. The harmless-looking sea cucumber (probably the

Scuba divers beware: perhaps the most venomous of all vertebrates, there are at least 50 species of sea snakes harmful or deadly to humans, many of them swimming in reefs and amongst seaweed just off shore. Seen here, the olive sea snake – which grows to 6 feet and is related to the cobra – has a venom against which no antidote exists.

most common creature of the undersea world) excretes poisonous sticky threads which can cause blindness in humans. It has a strange habit of eviscerating itself when under attack or stressed – squirting all its internal organs, including its stomach and intestines, through its anus. It also casts off all attached structures, such as tentacles, gonads and anterior ends. But the empty hull, composed of just skin and muscle, can regrow in about a month.

There is no doubt that the reef is a dangerous place. Much of it is covered with animals attached to the bottom with no ability to escape their enemies. Over millennia, many of these species have evolved an astounding variety of defences. None is more strange than the sea squirt that manufactures sulphuric acid in globules and transports it to the body surface. Any predator is in for a shock after one sour burning bite. If that isn't enough, the animal concentrates the poisonous metal, vanadium, enough to kill a horse! Anemones do not kill humans as far as is known but do cause a painful, slow-healing rash called 'sponge fisherman's disease'. Hydroids like fire or stinging corals can also be extremely poisonous, causing much pain to people who break off pieces, leaving them with coral poisoning. They suffer from searing burns that are hard to heal and leave permanent scars.

Another common animal, the Plexaura sea whip, produces large amounts of the very biologically active hormone, prostaglandin. This hormone is found in all animals, but usually in trace quantities. The Plexaura sea whip is a few per cent prostaglandin – any creature that eats it begins to retch and never returns for a second meal. Even the humble bristle worm can be dangerous, although not often lethal. When threatened, it poisons its enemies with its nose – a retractable four-fanged proboscis that it prods them with, causing paralysis – while the common bloodworm stings more severely than a bee.

Curiouser and curiouser . . .

The discovery of 'warm springs' on the sea floor opened up a whole new world of undersea life. In 1977 the US research ship *Knorr* had towed strobe lights and a camera on the sea floor one and a half miles down in the eastern Pacific Ocean, 200 miles northeast of the Galapagos Islands. Captured on film was a series of awesome images: a field of sea floor warm springs where colonies of huge shelled animals thrived.

Such warm water 'fountains' had never been seen before on the sea bed; while giant clams and mussels had never been suspected of living below the depth of sunlight penetration. Foot-long white clams, huge brown mussels and white crabs clung to the rocks around the warm spring. The US Navy submersible *Alvin* was later to descend into the depths of this pitch-black world. It revealed animals that resembled dandelions gone to seed; white-stalked tube worms with bright red tops; and carpets of what seemed to be bacteria. Equally puzzling was what these creatures could possibly eat to survive on their sea floor oasis. Further research showed that, astonishingly, they lived off hydrogen sulphide which bubbled up from the subterranean vents.

Far more lethal than the shark are the numerous poisonous fish in the sea. It is estimated that of the 25,000 fish species, 100 are poisonous to humans. Most dangerous in the cool-water regions are the weever fish. They go under many guises and names: sea cat, sand eel, adderpike, sting bull, blackfin, abo, foersing, petermanchen, ragno, meerlan and many more. Found mostly off the coasts of Europe, Africa and South America, they are small (a maximum of 18 inches long) and inflict one of the most painful stings of any animal. Generally they live buried in mud or sand of bays and are often stepped on. They thrust out long venomous spines from dorsal fins and gill covers that deliver instant and excruciating pain. Usually they will attack other small sea creatures but, aggressive for all their size, if slightly disturbed they will also

A stone fish – as ugly as it looks, found in Indo-Pacific seas, it lies in wait buried in mud or sand. When trodden on, it injects often fatal neurotoxins through thirteen jagged spines on its back, which are so sharp they can pierce shoes.

swim out, spines vibrating, and take on a diver or a bather. The pain of the sting is so intense for half an hour that divers have pleaded for death to end their suffering – one diver actually cut off his little finger – while another plunged his hand in fire. After a few hours the pain eases but is followed by fever, nausea, convulsions and even death. In September 1998 a British teenager died while snorkelling off Majorca; it is thought he was stung by a spider fish, a relative of the weever. In a single week of July 1998 alone, 200 people enjoying a summer break were stung by weevers at Cromer, Norfolk, fifteen severely enough to be hospitalized. Recovery can take months. Although the weever is good to eat, care must be taken, since the spines deliver poison even when the fish is dead.

The stone or scorpion fish, found in Indo-Pacific waters, injects neurotoxin poisons through thirteen jagged spines in its back which are so sharp they can easily pierce ordinary shoes. These ugly spines and warts on its back, enveloped in slime and algae, disguise it to resemble a small red and grey rock when buried in the mud or bottom sand. A formidable creature, its stings cause excruciating pain, delirium and sometimes death. Any pressure on these dorsal-fin spines pushes down the layer of skin (called the integumentary sheath) under each spine, releasing venom from a gland concealed below. A number of divers and bathers, especially off Australian beaches, have stepped on them and died within hours. Even when cast up on the beach they are dangerous since they can live out of the water for ten to twelve hours and often lie exposed in tidal pools.

A group of venomous creatures which are not true fishes includes the spiny dogfish, ratfish and sting ray. The spiny dogfish is a small shark, just 3–5 feet long, that lives in the North Atlantic and North Pacific. Sharp-grooved spines at the front of its

This blue-spotted stingray is small, but can still inflict severe pain. Many types of sting ray grow to a considerable size and inflict serious wounds with their large and venomous tail spines.

dorsal fins deliver venom to many fishermen trying to loose it from hooks. The stab wounds are always painful, sometimes lasting for days. Deaths have been reported although not verified. Ratfish possess a sharp serrated spine at the base of the dorsal fin that delivers poison which always causes painful swelling, though not death.

Sting rays cause up to 1,500 injuries a year, according to one study, more than all other fish combined. There are seven families of dangerous sting rays common to the shallow waters of all tropical and temperate seas and many thousands of rays often literally cover the bottom, wounding people who step on their whiplike tails. Poisonous spines at the base of the tail often remain embedded in victims, causing more anguish. The most dangerous ones are the true whiptails. Some are immense: spotted eagle rays measure up to 8 feet across their wings and weigh 800 pounds – while Australian giant rays are 7 by 14 feet, and weigh 700 pounds – with proportionately large spines that not only inject poison but also can inflict great tissue damage, ripping gashes over 6 inches long in victims.

Legends and horror movies are full of stories about some monster that lies asleep at the bottom of a lake for thousands of years until something causes it to wake. In the estuary of the Noose River of North Carolina where it flows to join the sea this scenario has come true – the monster has awoken; and the result could be catastrophic.

The monster is *Fisteria faecidida* – the fish killer. It is not itself a sea creature; and it is so small that we can't see it. It can change its shape, and it can attack through the air. It is killing not just millions, but billions of fish. The terrifying thing is that it can attack humans.

Mysterious fish massacres first started in 1987. The signs were easy to spot. The water turned brown, then it foamed. A sickly sweet smell seemed to drift over the surface – and then the fish started to go crazy. At first it was as if they were trying to escape whatever it was in the water that was attacking them. You could look down and see them develop open wounds as you watched. They leaped in the air, stood on their tails and spun in a death spiral sometimes for minutes, sometimes for an hour before dying. The one thing they did not do was escape – escape to the open sea that was tantalizingly close.

Marine biologist Dr Joanne Birkholder started to investigate; but at first, although she had samples of the dead fish in her lab and could identify the one-celled bacterium that was causing the damage, she couldn't find it in samples of river water and she needed that link. She didn't suspect that she had a cunning killer on her hands, one that had learned how to hide itself. Eventually, Dr Birkholder managed to get a sample of water at the height of a fish kill and into her laboratory fast.

What she saw under the microscope chilled her. Like a science fiction chameleon, the bacterium could take on twenty-four entirely different life forms – it could even make itself ninety times bigger – and all instantaneously. When the live bacteria were fed a drop of human blood, a feeding frenzy took place. The *Fisteria* cells excitedly spun around, grabbed hold of the red blood cells and consumed them.

Despite that, it was thought that since this was not a germ or a parasite it couldn't live in the human body. Then people working on the river started to get sick. They grew disoriented and lethargic; they developed skin lesions – in fact, one river worker was called 'leopard-man' because of the state of his skin. Dr Birkholder herself developed the symptoms. She installed very tight security – workers at the lab were masked and gloved and dressed in protective clothing. New air conditioning was installed.

Despite these precautions, lab director Howard Glasgow developed strange symptoms similar to Alzheimer's disease, together with skin lesions over his body. Finally he collapsed. In hospital, he was diagnosed as suffering acute neurologic trauma. Tests showed that he had breathed *Fisteria* into his lungs through a badly vented air conditioner that fed air from the laboratory straight over his desk. There was no cure; all the doctors could do was tell him to rest. Eventually, after many months away from the lab, away from *Fisteria*, Glasgow gradually did get better. Today, he is not permitted to go anywhere near it. No other similar bacteria can create airborne toxins – this was a terrifying monster that had been unleashed.

Dr Birkholder had discovered that *Fisteria* went into action when schools of fish came in from the sea and lingered to feed in the estuary. When it detected enough fish, it rose up from the bottom in the column and attacked them with the five or more poisons in its arsenal. One poison doped and disoriented the fish, while another stripped it of its skin and scales so it could feed on the fish's blood and tissues – exactly as it first disoriented, then fed on, humans.

Terrifyingly, fish kill is now occurring in the once wild and beautiful Chesapeake Bay and off Florida. What had changed *Fisteria* from a dormant organism that had lain quietly at the bottom of tidal estuaries for millions of years into a ferocious killer? It was discovered that people are to blame. The Noose River had become the runoff and dumping ground for anything upstream. 'Send it out to the sea – let the sea take care of it,' seemed to be the opinion. So everything from nutrient-rich sewage plants, to farms, to waste from the growing number of residential communities, had entered the estuary and dropped to the bottom – to nourish and awaken a savage monster that we do not know how to control.

chapter six

surviving the savage seas

For those in peril on the sea, as the deeply emotive mariner's hymn goes, survival is always a matter of faith, hope, charity – and luck. The faith and hope are the prayers that men utter when in desperate straits; the charity is the selfless aid they get from lifeboat and helicopter rescue crews; and luck is in the lap of the gods. Men on distressed ships and lifeboat crews do the bravest things they can; they can fight against all odds, all sense even, but the sea is always totally in control.

The badges awarded for bravery to British lifeboatmen have this prayer: 'Let not the deep swallow me up'. It could as well be 'Let me help others be not swallowed up' – lifeboat crews around the world offer a service that often puts their own lives at risk. Many are volunteers and funded by the public, as in Britain; but however funded, all members are dedicated to the preservation of life. They must undergo stringent training to be able to cope with emergencies at sea, where conditions could be dire. This final chapter acknowledges the huge tradition of service, skill and sacrifice by following two stories: one is about a school in the USA that trains lifeboat crews, while the other remembers the heroism of a British crew who gave their lives in an attempt to rescue others. In these two examples, man's ingenuity, technology and courage in the face of danger are emblematic of his struggle against the elements.

Senior Chief Instructor Cliff Hohl of the United States National Lifeboat School.

PREPARING FOR THE WORST

'This area is ugly, dangerous and ferocious. The Bar punishes human frailties without mercy. You never know where the next break is coming from. You cannot beat the bar. The best you can hope for is a stalemate. Training, experience and skill may be the only thing standing between a successful sortie or a serious mishap,' says Senior Chief Instructor Cliff Hohl, of the National Lifeboat School.

The mouth of the Columbia River on the Pacific coast of the United States contains some of the most treacherous surf in the world. This river is fed by a watershed the size of the whole of France. At the river's mouth its billions of gallons of fresh water collide with the incoming ocean, its towering waves and hurricane force winds generated by storms off Alaska. The result is a confusion of cross currents and mountainous waves of crushing force that strikes fear into the hearts of sailors. It has earned the nickname 'The Graveyard of the Pacific', a wild cauldron in which entire ships have been torn apart beneath the feet of their crew. Debris litters the river mouth and more than 150 ships strew the sea bed, with some 700 lives claimed. This is where the surf training school of the US Coast Guard is situated. The location is aptly named: Cape Disappointment.

The course in heavy-weather surf training is the only one of its kind in the world. All the recruits are seasoned coxswains, but to graduate they must operate rescue craft in the most hostile of conditions.

Coast guard instructor Darrin Wallace describes it:

'The first time we take them out there, we demo exactly what they're supposed to do and we throw the student on the wheel. We're telling them how to get in a surf zone without taking a break on their beam. Once they get into the area that they want, we're making them stay on a range, which is basically station-keeping, staying in one spot, and they go right back out.

'There's a lot of stress involved and the noise of the surf because it's pretty loud, and the engines – they're very loud also. You get your crewmen on either side of the boat, screaming at you, where you're at the range, waves are coming. They can get overloaded a little bit, get that deer in the headlights look. But if they do it, after a while it starts getting easier.

'Sometimes you get some students who are kind of a little cocky, they think they know a little more than they do. And they get slapped really hard. It kinds of opens up their eyes a little bit and brings down that cockiness.'

Above Furious waves and currents meet off Cape Disappointment, Washington State, where the National Lifeboat School is located.

Below Coast guard students are trained in real surf conditions at the National Lifeboat School, in the dangerous waters where the mighty Columbia River meets storm waves from Alaska.

Students from the National Lifeboat School have to be trained in the roughest seas in order to cope with the real circumstances of a disaster at sea.

The swells rolling ashore here have been generated by storms a thousand miles out in the Pacific. As the sea bed becomes more shallow, the waves slow down and bunch together. When their height becomes critical, when the sea depth is less than half the wave length, they start to break. All the energy of their long journey from the deep ocean is thrown into these first breakers. Yet, in the apparent chaos of the surf-zone, there is a kind of order.

Cliff Hohl says it is important that they train in these hazardous conditions to give real experience, to test the men and women to their limits – to show them some of what they can expect. You can never replicate the exact conditions of a truly perilous rescue, but you can let lifeboat crew gauge their own strengths and weaknesses.

The surf off the Columbia is an ideal training ground. Chief Hohl describes it: 'It takes a long time to really read and identify the patterns. We have plunging breakers which I would consider the most dangerous. They can take out your windows and do structural damage to the vessel. Then you also have sloughing breaks – when it breaks it just comes down its own face – they can also take out windows depending how big the white water is, so once again it's going to take skill, surfmanship, on the part of the coxswain to take that wave.'

Mankind steers a perilous course in his relationship with the sea. He can bring to bear intelligence, guile and the hard-won wisdom of generations, but he still competes at his peril with the raw power of the ocean. Instructor Wallace knows the language of the sea. Long experience has taught him to read the waves.

'*Waves come in a set or series, they come between four and six waves at a time. And then when you get that lull, that's when you can manoeuvre left or right, or inbound or outbound. We teach them always to keep their bow square on into the surf or swell. The boat takes the surf best when it's square to the swell. When I first started working these boats a surfman told me, "Never go out there to challenge the water, never play with Mother Earth otherwise she'll bite you in the butt and you'll pay the price."*'

The school runs courses in winter conditions, between January and March, for heavy-weather training. This course, which trains only six officers at a time, is considered one of the toughest around and is open only to seasoned coxswains who have driven lifeboats for at least six months. It is hard and testing. The first day involves the coxswains swimming ashore in rough seas and having to tow boats through heavy seas both day and night. They practise passing lines and moving equipment from one boat to another, the kind of risky manoeuvre which is normal in real-life rescues.

On the sixth day, weather permitting, the six coxswains practise rescuing a man overboard, through a range of dangerous manoeuvres which often involve the boat rolling through 360 degrees. Three students in each boat are strapped in these boats, which are designed to right themselves within fifteen seconds. This part of the course is always considered the most dangerous and challenging and is always carried out in exceptional surf. This part of the course is obligatory because students must prove they can operate in the most hostile of conditions. If the Pacific becomes uncharacteristically calm so the manoeuvre can't be achieved, they don't graduate until it is.

The new 47-foot motor lifeboats are designed to handle waves of up to 20 feet; far higher than the 6-foot minimum the course stipulates the students must train in to qualify as 'surfmen' or advanced coxswains. In some courses, students have gone out in 12- and 15-foot waves. But here they prefer their instructors to go out in the deepest and most dangerous surf to show how it's really done. Chief Hohl says: 'We don't want any mishaps among the students or instructors during training sessions. They'll get the real thing once they go back to their stations.'

ENDURING THE WORST

No practice, no training, can prepare a lifeboat crew for waves of up to 100 feet high. Nothing. The crew of the Penlee lifeboat off the coast of Cornwall met waves of 60 to 70 feet which grew still higher when the *Union Star* was washed into the cliffs that dark night just before Christmas on 19 December 1981.

At eight o'clock on the morning of that day – a Saturday – Coast Guard Colin Sturman had just come off duty and was driving home from Falmouth. As he drove up the hill out of the town, he noticed in his rear-view mirror the spectacular colour of the dawn sky. He stopped in a lay-by at the top of the hill, got out of his car and, with a

The original Penlee lifeboat was lost with all hands one stormy night just before Christmas, in December 1981. The replacement boat is seen here with a new crew as it slides down the slip during a training session.

sense of awe and foreboding, stared towards the east. He recalled the saying, 'Red sky at night – shepherd's delight; red sky in the morning, shepherd's warning.' And what's a warning to shepherds applies in spades to sailors... He says: 'It really was the most frightening red sky I have ever seen. I remember thinking that the possibility of some bad weather coming in seemed imminent.'

Sturman returned to duty that same afternoon, to take over the 1600 watch. The weather wasn't very bad, but by 1800 the shipping forecast was for southerly gales veering to the west and increasing to 'severe gale 9 – storm force 10'. Mick Moreton, master of a coastal freighter, the *Union Star*, radioed in almost immediately after the storm warning, giving his position as being off the dangerous Wolfe Rock Lighthouse some eight miles offshore, and informing the guard that he had engine failure. He said he was calling as a precaution since he was confident of getting his engines restarted.

Sturman went through the usual procedure of informing the rescue co-ordinators at Plymouth for a helicopter to be brought in readiness; the Penlee Lifeboat was asked to come to a state of readiness – at that time, known as anticipatory; and they spoke to Captain Buurman of salvage tug the *Noord Holland* in Mount's Bay through the Land's End radio asking if he would be willing and able to proceed to assist the *Union Star*. Later, Captain Buurman, who had been at sea for many years, was to say that it was the worst weather he had ever known. As the weather worsened, a helicopter took off and confirmed the position of the *Union Star*, at the same time coast guards, positioned on the cliffs of Land's End as observers, were struggling with the spray that was lifted high over the cliff top on the wind and blinding them.

Pilot Russ Smith was assigned as a duty search and rescue crew and aircraft commander that evening. He was to have had dinner out with his wife. On the way to taking his children to the baby-sitter, he could sense the weather worsening. On arrival, his wife rang him and told him the base had called and he was on standby. He returned home with the children. Then he went to the station to prepare and wait.

It takes thirty-five minutes to get one of the big Sea King helicopters ready to take off. When the crew became airborne they noticed the wind was quite a bit stronger than their brief. Conditions were worsening as they headed out to sea to report on the position of the 110-foot distressed ship and see if they could assist. When they arrived, the ship was 2 miles off the coast and drifting sideways towards it in a 45-foot confused sea. Smith says: 'When we arrived, the captain asked if we could take a woman and her two teenage daughters off the ship. It was a flat-bottomed vessel and was rolling terribly.'

The ship was rolling and pitching so violently in the sea, with waves crashing over the wheelhouse, that three attempts to lower crew winchman Steven Marlowe failed. They had to avoid the wildly swinging ship's mast; and at the same time not come down so low that high spray or gale-force winds would throw them into the cliffs. The winds were so strong that as the rescue rope was trailed below the helicopter, it was blown almost horizontally off direction.

Winchman Marlowe had just disembarked from aircraft carrier HMS *Invincible* to join 820 Squadron on Land's End for search and rescue during the winter period. The

The *Union Star* was wrecked at Tatar-Dhû, near Land's End, Cornwall, in furious seas. The Penlee lifeboat was lost when the ship rolled over onto it during a heroic attempt to rescue passengers and crew.

weather was so bad the night he was called to the *Union Star* that nobody in his home had even wanted to go out to the coal bunker to get coal and the fire had gone out. He had sensed that he would be called out. 'It was very nasty, completely overcast, so very black, no light, no moon. There was a horizontal rain with the wind directly on to the cliffs. That was part of the problem. When we went low we felt we would be blown directly onto the cliffs.'

A Sea King is a huge, stable helicopter, as big as a delivery truck. Sitting above the *Union Star*, they had what Marlowe describes as a God's eye view. They had become part of the environment, part of the disaster.

The helicopter got into a position above the tanker where Marlowe could trail a 100-foot rope on deck. But the crewman on the deck below didn't seem able to grasp the rope – he did get it into his hands on one occasion, but the ship dropped and he lost his grip. Marlowe volunteered to be lowered down 15 feet below the helicopter to hold the rope in order to give it a little more length.

'It actually didn't work well because of all the violent swinging and the motion of the aircraft… we persuaded them to bring the lady out, the first person we'd attempt to rescue, and I distinctly remember I am hanging under the aircraft, no longer on the intercom so I can't talk to my crew and it's their job to get me on the deck. It's my job to concentrate on where I'm going and then to actually effect the rescue. I was looking at this brand-new, bright-green painted deck, and the lady was standing against the bulkhead and she had got on bright pink court shoes. To this day I remember this vivid image. It was so incongruous to see these court shoes in this wild environment.'

Marlowe was not able to get on deck. As he tried one last time, he saw the lifeboat coming. The helicopter stood off because it's always considered too dangerous to work over the top of a lifeboat and endanger the crew.

Although he was only seventeen years old, Neil Brockman was a member of the Penlee lifeboat crew in the village of Mousehole, as was his father. That day he had been at work on a 32-foot fishing boat out of Newlyn. After work, he went home and watched television with the family. They could all hear a gale blowing outside and remarked the boat might be called out. Neil's father, who had been at a football match, came in and joined them around the fire,

Present Penlee lifeboat cox Neil Brockman and his mother, Jacqueline, shortly after he had been awarded a bronze medal for bravery in conjunction with Senner lifeboat. At just 17 years old, Neil was turned away on the night of the disaster, while his father went and was lost, being awarded the RNLI bronze medal posthumously. When the new lifeboat came, Neil volunteered at once.

watching television. At about 6.30 the phone rang. It was the coast guard saying that a ship had lost power and the lifeboat was on standby. Neil and his father stayed at home because the boathouse was not heated and would be too cold to wait in. Besides, Mousehole is a very small place, so all the crew were within reach of the lifeboat station.

They were called at about 8 o'clock; when the maroon went, they moved fast. At the boathouse, the place was crowded, because everybody locally was wanting to help, to deal with the chains that held the boat in place and generally to be on hand if needed. All of them noticed that the sea conditions were the worst any of them could remember. When Coxswain Trevelyan Richards picked his crew, young Neil put himself forward, as did everybody.

'I said I would go, but he turned me down, saying that he already had one member of the family on the boat, which was his way of saying he didn't want two of us in the same family dead. I was gutted that I wasn't chosen. I think Trevelyan knew... a premonition. He said, "I only want one from each family going tonight." The old man... Dad... winked at me when he jumped aboard the boat. He looked at me and gave me a wink then carried on with his jobs. The conditions were very, very bad. It was unbelievable. To actually get that boat to sea from the slip was no mean feat. It was an excellent piece of seamanship to actually get the boat in the water.'

Reporter Andrew Besley had been talking to the coast guard at Falmouth about a local yacht disaster when he was told that a small freighter on its maiden voyage had engine failure off Land's End. At that stage, the ship's master, Mick Moreton, was so reassuring and calm that nobody thought the problem would escalate. When Besley learned that the Penlee crew had been called out, he drove to the lifeboat station.

'I could see there was activity going on. As I ran down the steps I heard the pin come out and the boat rumble down and hit the water and away she went. I couldn't believe it. The sea on that slip was horrendous. I walked back up the steps and watched the boat going between Mousehole Island and away into the distance. I decided to drive to the cliffs to watch.

'Up on the cliffs the Mousehole Christmas lights were shining through the rain, proclaiming the message "Happy Christmas" to passing ships. As I drove up towards the lights the "Happy" fused. It just left the word "Christmas". It was the first of several extraordinary things that happened and carried on happening that night.'

Later, Besley was told that technically speaking, what he had observed was impossible. But it happened just the same, round about the time the lifeboat reached the stricken *Union Star*.

On the cliffs, as he watched, he said it all seemed like a dream. The sea was so enormous that surf was sweeping up to the top of the cliffs. By now, the ship was below them, foundering on rocks. The position was so precarious that the Sea King had to stand off, but its big lights illuminated the shiny black basalt cliffs and the wreck like a ghastly theatre.

> '*You could occasionally see a little figure come out of the wheelhouse and then go back in. My eyes and face were so full of rain... then it would ease a bit and you would get a vision. It was like a dream. Then suddenly the rain would clear and you would see this horrendous scene down there. It was obvious that the boat was going aground within minutes. But Trevelyan Richards brought the lifeboat in, holding his bows against the sides of the boat.*
>
> '*Suddenly an enormous roller appeared behind and he obviously saw this, that it was going to engulf him, and with tremendous skill he went astern with the lifeboat. I thought he was going to get through and over it, but the crest of the wave picked him up and physically dropped the lifeboat across the* Union Star. *Now I have a background of being trained as a boat builder, so I had some appreciation as to what that would do to a wooden-hulled lifeboat.*'

The next wave lifted it off, and the lifeboat went slowly astern, inching its way. Richards seemed in command. He seemed to know what he was doing. The *Union Star* was heeled over on its side, presenting a great slab of steel ramp. Astonishingly, using a massive wave, Richards aimed the boat straight up the hull, to the top. It wasn't far enough. He went back and did it again. For a brief moment he hung there – long enough to take off four people.

The last radio message from him said, 'I have four people.' Then the lifeboat slipped back off the hull. He tried it again – and the *Union Star* seemed to heave and fell back on top of the lifeboat.

Winchman Steven Marlow describes what he saw from the Sea King:

> '*The* Union Star *was right over on its side, so you've got a great slab side of the vessel and the lifeboat was right up the side of the vessel. I was horrified by what I was watching because it looked dreadful from a helicopter and imagining what the scene was like from where those men were on the lifeboat is beyond me. We saw them make a number of runs. I certainly saw something orange disappear between the two boats when they were alongside at one stage. Whether it was a lifejacket or a person we'll never know.*
>
> '*The bravery of the lifeboat crew is unimaginable. It was pitch black... just the shiny cliffs. There was a dreadful feeling when it went quiet on the radio.*'

It was as if somebody had turned the lights out. On the clifftop, Andrew Besley was gutted. He stood watching into the darkness, hoping and praying that a light would appear on the crest of a wave. No light ever appeared. He thought perhaps the lifeboat had gone round the corner of the cove – that it was safe. 'I stood for ten minutes, a quarter of an hour, realizing the enormity of what had happened. In my own heart I knew that the lifeboat had gone. I walked back to the car, stunned, shocked with the sheer horror of it.'

In Mousehole everybody was waiting. Tension and fear were in the air and on their faces. Skippers from other ships, other lifeboats, came, just wanting to be there, walking up and down, waiting. In the desperation of their hopes, wild rumours sprang up and then died. They were calling on their radios, 'Trevelyan, come over to us, boy, are you all right? Do you want us to come out and help you?'

But there was no answer to those calls. Bill Tonkin, the skipper of another boat, called and called, and finally he looked up and said with quiet certainty, 'She's gone.' It was a chilling moment. But still no one would believe it.

The coast guard sent out lifeboats from the Lizard, St Mary's and Mullion Cove to search the area. All returned to station with no news. Coast guard officer Colin Sturman says: 'We thought the lifeboat might have been on its way back with the survivors because there were several reports both from the scene and from our visual lookout from Penza Point to say that they actually could see the lifeboat's lights steaming back towards Newlyn.'

In the boathouse at Mousehole, they still waited and prayed. The cliff rescue team arrived to wait, as they all were, with water leaping up the slipway, hard rain in their faces, staring out towards Mousehole Island, waiting for a sign.

And there was a sign, something that made the air almost electric. Andrew Besley says: 'The spray from the waves was breaking some 40... 50... 60 feet right up the harbour wall. We stood back and all of a sudden, silhouetted in the white wall of water we saw a section of a lifeboat. It came bang down the edge of the slipway. The men ran forward and horror registered on all those faces. They said, "It's her." The dark blue of a lifeboat hull on the outside of the cross diagonal planking, white on the inside. There was only one boat that had come from.'

More and more bits came round the harbour wall. The Penlee lifeboat had come home.

The fight goes on

After the Penlee lifeboat was lost with all hands, the Royal National Lifeboat Institution asked the villagers of Mousehole if they wanted another lifeboat. The RNLI asked the question because so many men had been lost from this one small fishing community that possibly the people would not wish to endure the risk of another tragedy. But the whole village said of course they wanted one, even though the crew would have to be built up again almost from scratch. Neil Brockman was one of the first to volunteer for the new crew, and is now the coxswain.

production team

A series like *Savage Seas* can be made only with the help of many, many people from different spheres.

It could never have been made without the assistance and advice of oceanographers and other experts on the world's seas, who helped direct us to the places and people to film. Nor could we have told the many personal stories that enrich the series, giving it both drama and humanity, without the co-operation and patience of those people who have found themselves often quite unexpected, and certainly unwilling, witnesses to the power of the savage seas. Filming on four continents, on (or sometimes in) three great oceans, would not have been possible without the technical skill and expertise of many television professionals. The names of the many survivors and experts to whom we talked are mostly included in the text of the book; the people on the other side of the camera were these:

Camera	Tim Pollard	**Dubbing editors**	Jack Dardis
	Danny Rohrer		Hilary Wyatt
Underwater camera	Frazier Nivens	**Production co-ordinators**	Del Bowen Hayes
	Andrew Mann		Gareth Williams
Sound	Mark Atkinson		
	Steve Hunter	**Assistant producers**	Gerrie Byrne
			Emma Hawley
Assistant camera	Keith Staniforth		Birgitte Johnson
	Malcolm Keys		James Millar
	Chris Jones		
		Executive producer for Thirteen/WNET	Bill Grant
Music	Howard Davidson		Beth Hoppe
Film researcher	Maggi Cook	**Producer-directors**	Bill Lyons
			Andrew Serraillier
Titles and graphic design	Paul Kearton		
	Simon Blackledge	**Series producer**	Liz McLeod
	Alex Jeffries		
		Executive producer	Bill Jones
Film editors	David Cresswell		
	Peter Hallworth		

select bibliography

The basis for this book was the considerable original research done for the *Savage Seas* television series; however, if this book stimulates an interest in the sea, then the following list may be helpful for those who wish to expand their reading. (Many of these books can be found through amazon.co.uk)

Lloyd's Register of Shipping – Lloyd's of London 1998

The Discovery of the 'Titanic' – Robert D. Ballard; Rick Archbold, NY 1998

The Book of Waves – Drew Kampion *et al*; Robert Rinehart, Hawaii 1997

Deep-Ocean Journeys – Cindy Lee Van Dover; Helix, NY 1997

Exploring the Wonders of the Deep – Jacques-Yves Cousteau; Lois Markham, NY 1997

Deep Atlantic – Richard Ellis; Knopf, NY 1996

Oceanography & Seamanship – W. G. Van Dorn; NY 1993

Deep Oceans Circulation – T. Teramoto; Elsevier Oceanography, No. 59 1993

The Ocean Almanac – Robert Hendrickson; Hutchinson Reference 1992

The Sea Around Us – Rachel Carson; OUP 1991

The Strange World of Deep-Sea Vents – R.V. Fodor; Enslow, NJ 1991

Seawater – A Delicate Balance; A. Lee Meyerson; Enslow, NJ 1990

Disasters at Sea – Milton H Watson; Patrick Stephen, 1987

The Cape Run – Mitchell & Sawyer; I. Dalton, 1984

Disaster at Sea – Edgar Haine; Cornwall Books, 1983

The Earth and Its Oceans – Alyn C. Duxbury; Addison Wesley, NY 1971

The Story of Maps – Lloyd Brown; Little, Brown, Boston, 1940

Half Mile Down – William Beebe; Harcourt Brace, NY 1934

Icewalk – Robert Swan; Cape, London 1990

The Oceans Atlas – Anita Ganeri; Dorling Kindersley, London 1994

A Night To Remember – Walter Lord; Penguin Books, London 1978

Antarctica – Lonely Planet Travel Survival Kit; Lonely Planet Publications, Head Office: PO Box 617 Hawthorn Vic 3122 Australia; UK: 10 Barley Mow Passage, London W4 4PH

Arctic Papers – Scott Polar Research Institute, Cambridge

The *National Geographic* magazine has published many articles about the sea during the past twenty years. A complete collection of these can be found in the British Library.

Thanks also to Readers' Digest for access to their archives in search of the unusual and gripping story or anecdote.

index

(All numbers in **bold** refer to illustrations)

picture acknowledgements

AKG London / E. Lessing: 17 (top & bottom), 18

Associated Press: 131

Beken of Cowes: 47, 57

Andrew Besley: 205

Boards Magazine: John Carter 77 (top & bottom); Darrell Wong 78 (main & inset); 79

Bridgeman Art Library: University of Witwatersrand, South Africa 18 –19; National Museum of Ancient Art, Lisbon, 18 (inset); Christies Images, London, 42 (top); 73 (main); National Maritime Museum, London, 103; Bibliotheque Royale de Belgique, Brussels, 147; Scuola di San Giorgio Degli Schiavoni, Venice, 183.

Bruce Coleman: M. Freeman 10–11; Geoff Dove 52; Dr Eckart Pott 111; Fred Bruemmer 120; Jeff Foot Productions 122; Pacific Stock 166 – 7; Erik Bjurstrom 168

Dan Burton: 161

Corbis/ UPI Bettman: 94

Cornwall & Isle of Scilly Press: 206

Cunnards Archive, University of Liverpool: 49

Frank Lane Picture Agency: Silvestris 90; Steve McCutcheon 136 (top); Chris Newton 191 (b); Ian Cartwright 194, 196

Frank Spooner Pictures: 67 (top); Gamma 92-93, 97,155

Granada Television: Emma Hawley 22, 138, 139, 200, 201 (top & bottom), 202; James Millar 31, 81, 82, 159 (bottom); Mark Atkinson 44

Image Bank: Inner Light 59

Dr J. E. Jones: 43

Kobal Collection: 72

Mariner's Museum, Newport News, VA The: 24

Mary Evans Picture Library: 35, 42 (bottom), 69 (bottom), 73 (inset), 114 (top & bottom), 116, 148, 163, 189, 190

Robert McGuiggan: 168 (bottom), 172, 174

Mirror Syndication International: 67 (bottom)

National Geographic: Richard T. Nowitz 37, James L. Amos 135, Chris Johns 136 (bottom), Thomas J. Abercrombie 149 (top)

Network Photographers/ Jillian Edelstein: 164, 165

Jerome Nickerson: 46, 50, 54

Oxford Scientific Films: Doug Allen 25 (top); Ronald Toms 41; 91

P.A. News Ltd: 68 (top)

Peter Newark's American Pictures: 15, 16

Planet Earth Pictures: Ivor Edmonds 13; Marty Snyderman 32; Jean Guichard 60-61; Steve Bloom 84–85; Richard Coomber 96; Norman Cobley 106-7; Peter Scoones 144-5, 185; Kurt Amsler 168, 181; Gary Bell 191, 193; Andrew Mounter 192; Herwarth Voigtmann 195.

Popperfoto: 124, 153, 156, 159 (top)

Rex Features: 28, 66; Sipa Press 100 (main); 127; 178

Royal Geographic Society: Remote Source/ Roger Mear 109

Royal Navy Submarine Museum: 160

Science Photo Library: Martin Bond 39

Still Pictures: L. Funkhouser 104

Stock Market: Ben Simmons 14

Sygma: 154 (top & bottom)

Telegraph Colour Library: Masterfile 2/198-199; Alex Williams 7; C. Michaels 33; D. Sim 63; Steve Bloom 84-5; Al Satterwhite 102

Richard Thelan: 169 (top)

Tony Stone Images: Ernest Braun 52

Topham: 25 (bottom); Associated Press 100 (inset); 128; 149 (bottom); 204

Woodfall Wild Images: Mike Lane 182

Zoological Society of London: 184 188